INVITATION

TO

POETRY

AN ANTHOLOGY FOR JUNIOR STUDENTS

SELECTED AND EDITED BY

J. L. GILL AND L. H. NEWELL

INSTRUCTORS IN ENGLISH

THE UNIVERSITY OF TORONTO SCHOOLS

TORONTO
THE MACMILLAN COMPANY OF CANADA LIMITED

PREFACE

The poems in this anthology have been chosen for boys and girls in the junior high school. In making their selections, the editors have attempted to choose poetry that not only possesses poetic merit but also is suited to the interests and experiences of students at this particular age level. Except for those favourite poems that have proved their worth down through the years, all the selections in the book have been tested carefully in the classroom. This applies especially to the ones which are here included in a school anthology for the first time.

The book is divided into two parts, similar in length and organization, designed for use in consecutive school years. Each part contains forty poems, grouped under "Shorter Narratives" (nineteen), "Longer Narratives" (eight), and "Lyrics" (thirteen), and arranged, under each heading, in what is considered to be a convenient and attractive teaching order. In each part, ten poems are of Canadian authorship, nine are American and twenty-one are British. Approximately two-thirds of the poetry was written in the twentieth century.

The notes on the various poems provide necessary background information, explain literary references and give the meanings of terms that are not found in an ordinary pocket dictionary. The considerable detail into which they frequently go in these respects may be justified by the fact that many teachers have neither the time nor the facilities for searching out these facts on their own. These notes are not included with the thought that they should be studied methodically by the students. Rather, if they make the poems more vital and enjoyable they will achieve their basic purpose.

The editors wish to express their sincere thanks to the various teachers who so kindly recommended favourite poems, as well as to those who gave such helpful advice as to the nature and plan of the book. They are indebted especially to the different classes who studied and expressed their opinions on the many poems from which those in this anthology finally were selected.

J.L.G.
L.H.N.

Toronto, January, 1956.

CONTENTS

PART ONE

SHORTER NARRATIVES

slow gr. 10'0

vii

PART TWO

SHORTER NARRATIVES

viii

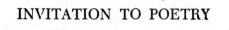

INVITATION TO POETRY

PART ONE

DUNKIRK

Will came back from school that day,
And he had little to say.
But he stood a long time looking down
To where the grey-green Channel water
Slapped at the foot of the little town,
And to where his boat, the *Sarah P*,
Bobbed at the tide on an even keel,
With her one old sail, patched at the leech,
Furled like a slattern down at heel.

He stood for a while above the beach;   10
He saw how the wind and current caught her.
He looked a long time out to sea.
There was steady wind and the sky was pale,
And a haze in the east that looked like smoke.

Will went back to the house to dress.
He was halfway through when his sister Bess,
Who was near fourteen and younger than he
By just two years, came home from play.
She asked him, "Where are you going, Will?"
He said, "For a good long sail."   20
"Can I come along?"
                "No, Bess," he spoke.
"I may be gone for a night and a day."
Bess looked at him.   She kept very still.
She had heard the news of the Flanders rout,
How the English were trapped above Dunkirk,
And the fleet had gone to get them out—
But everyone thought that it wouldn't work.
There was too much fear, there was too much doubt.

3

She looked at him and he looked at her.
They were English children, born and bred.   30
He frowned her down, but she wouldn't stir.
She shook her proud young head.
"You'll need a crew," she said.

They raised the sail on the *Sarah P*,
Like a penoncel on a young knight's lance,
And headed the *Sarah* out to sea,
To bring their soldiers home from France.

There was no command, there was no set plan,
But six hundred boats went out with them
On the grey-green waters, sailing fast,   40
River excursion and fisherman,
Tug and schooner and racing *M*,
And the little boats came following last.

From every harbour and town they went
Who had sailed their craft in the sun and rain,
From the South Downs, from the cliffs of Kent,
From the village street, from the country lane.
There are twenty miles of rolling sea
From coast to coast, by the seagull's flight,
But the tides were fair and the wind was free,   50
And they raised Dunkirk by the fall of night.

They raised Dunkirk with its harbour torn
By the blasted stern and the sunken prow;
They had raced for fun on an English tide,
They were English children bred and born,
And whether they lived or whether they died,
They raced for England now.

Bess was as white as the *Sarah*'s sail,
She set her teeth and smiled at Will.

4

He held his course for the smoky veil   60
Where the harbour narrowed thin and long.
The British ships were firing strong.

He took the *Sarah* into his hands,
He drove her in through fire and death
To the wet men waiting on the sands.
He got his load and he got his breath,
And she came about, and the wind fought her.

He shut his eyes and he tried to pray.
He saw his England where she lay,
The wind's green home, the sea's proud daughter,   70
Still in the moonlight, dreaming deep,
The English cliffs and the English loam—
He had fourteen men to get away,
And the moon was clear and the night like day
For planes to see where the white sails creep
Over the black water.

He closed his eyes and he prayed for her;
He prayed to the men who had made her great,
Who had built her land of forest and park,
Who had made the seas an English lake;   80
He prayed for a fog to bring the dark;
He prayed to get home for England's sake.
And the fog came down on the rolling sea,
And covered the ships with English mist.
The diving planes were baffled and blind.

For Nelson was there in the *Victory*,
With his one good eye, and his sullen twist,
And guns were out on *The Golden Hind*,
Their shot flashed over the *Sarah P*.
He could hear them cheer as he came about.   90
By burning wharves, by battered slips,

5

Galleon, frigate, and brigantine,
The old dead Captains fought their ships,
And the great dead Admirals led the line.
It was England's night, it was England's sea.

The fog rolled over the harbour key.
Bess held to the stays and conned him out.

And all through the dark, while the *Sarah's* wake
Hissed behind him, and vanished in foam,
There at his side sat Francis Drake,   **100**
And held him true and steered him home.

ROBERT NATHAN

LOCHINVAR

O, young Lochinvar is come out of the west,
Through all the wide Border his steed was the best,
And save his good broadsword he weapons had none;
He rode all unarmed, and he rode all alone.
So faithful in love, and so dauntless in war,
There never was knight like the young Lochinvar.

He stayed not for brake, and he stopped not for stone,
He swam the Eske river where ford there was none;
But, ere he alighted at Netherby gate,
The bride had consented, the gallant came late: **10**
For a laggard in love, and a dastard in war,
Was to wed the fair Ellen of brave Lochinvar.

So boldly he entered the Netherby hall,
Among bridesmen and kinsmen, and brothers and all:
Then spoke the bride's father, his hand on his sword

(For the poor craven bridegroom said never a word),
"O come ye in peace here, or come ye in war,
Or to dance at our bridal, young Lord Lochinvar?"

"I long wooed your daughter, my suit you denied;—
Love swells like the Solway, but ebbs like its tide— 20
And now I am come, with this lost love of mine,
To lead but one measure, drink one cup of wine.
There are maidens in Scotland more lovely by far,
That would gladly be bride to the young Lochinvar."

The bride kissed the goblet; the knight took it up,
He quaffed off the wine, and he threw down the cup,
She looked down to blush, and she looked up to sigh,
With a smile on her lips and a tear in her eye.
He took her soft hand, ere her mother could bar,—
"Now tread we a measure!" said young Lochinvar. 30

So stately his form, and so lovely her face,
That never a hall such a galliard did grace;
While her mother did fret, and her father did fume,
And the bridegroom stood dangling his bonnet and
    plume;
And the bridemaidens whispered, " 'Twere better by far
To have matched our fair cousin with young
    Lochinvar."

One touch to her hand, and one word in her ear,
When they reached the hall-door, and the charger stood
    near:
So light to the croupe the fair lady he swung,
So light to the saddle before her he sprung!   40
"She is won! we are gone, over bank, bush, and scaur;
They'll have fleet steeds that follow," quoth young
    Lochinvar.

There was mounting 'mong Græmes of the Netherby
clan;
Forsters, Fenwicks, and Musgraves, they rode and they
ran;
There was racing, and chasing, on Cannobie Lee,
But the lost bride of Netherby ne'er did they see.
So daring in love, and so dauntless in war,
Have ye e'er heard of gallant like young Lochinvar?

SIR WALTER SCOTT

THE SQUAD OF ONE

Sergeant Blue of the Mounted Police was a so-so kind of guy;
He swore a bit, and he lied a bit, and he boozed a bit on
the sly;
But he held the post at Snake Creek Bend in the good old
British way,
And a grateful country paid him about sixty cents a day.

Now the life of the North-West Mounted Police breeds an
all-round kind of man;
A man who can finish whatever he starts, and no matter
how it began;
A man who can wrestle a drunken bum, or break up a range
stampede—
Such are the men of the Mounted Police, and such are the
men they breed.

The snow lay deep at the Snake Creek post and deep to
east and west,
And the Sergeant had made his ten-league beat and settled
down to rest   **10**

8

In his two-by-four that they called a "post", where the flag
flew overhead,
And he took a look at his monthly mail, and this is the
note he read:

"To Sergeant Blue, of the Mounted Police, at the post at
Snake Creek Bend,
From U.S. Marshal of County Blank, greetings to you, my
friend:
They's a team of toughs give us the slip, though they shot
up a couple of blokes,
And we reckon they's hid in Snake Creek Gulch, and
posin' as farmer folks.

"Of all the toughs I ever saw I reckon these the worst,
So shoot to kill if you shoot at all, and be sure you do it first,
And send out your strongest squad of men and round them
up if you can,
For dead or alive we want them here. Yours truly, Jack
McMann."   **20**

And Sergeant Blue sat back and smiled, and his heart was
glad and free,
And he said, "If I round these beggars up it's another
stripe for me;
And promotion don't come easy to one of us Mounty chaps,
So I'll scout around tomorrow and I'll bring them in—
perhaps."

Next morning Sergeant Blue, arrayed in farmer smock and
jeans,
In a jumper sleigh he had made himself set out for the
evergreens
That grow on the bank of Snake Creek Gulch by a home-
stead shack he knew,
And a smoke curled up from the chimney-pipe to welcome
Sergeant Blue.

9

"Aha!" said Blue, "and who are you? Behold, the chimney
smokes,
But the boy that owns this homestead shack is up at
Okotoks; 30
And he wasn't expecting callers, for he left his key with me,
So I'll just drop in for an interview and we'll see what we
shall see!"

So he drove his horse to the shanty door and hollered a loud
"Good day,"
And a couple of men with fighting-irons came out beside
the sleigh;
And the Sergeant said, "I'm a stranger here and I've driven
a weary mile,
If you don't object I'll just sit down by the stove in the
shack a while."

Then the Sergeant sat and smoked and talked of the home
he had left down East,
And the cold and the snow, and the price of land, and the
life of man and beast,
But all of a sudden he broke it off with, "Neighbours, take
a nip?
There's a horn of the best you'll find out there in my
jumper, in the grip." 40

So one of the two went out for it, and as soon as he closed
the door
The Sergeant tickled the other one's ribs with the nose of
his forty-four;
"Now, fellow," he said, "you're a man of sense, and you
know when you're on the rocks,
And a noise as loud as a mouse from you and they'll take
you home in a box."

10

And he fastened the bracelets to his wrists, and his legs
with a halter-shank,
And he took his knife and he took his gun and he made
him safe as the bank,
And then he mustered Number Two in an Indian file
parade,
And he gave some brief directions — and Number Two
obeyed.

And when he had coupled them each to each and set them
down on the bed,
"It's a frosty day and we'd better eat before we go," he
said.   50
So he fried some pork and he warmed some beans, and he
set out the best he saw,
And he noted the price for the man of the house, according
to British law.

That night in the post sat Sergeant Blue, with paper and
pen in hand,
And this is the word he wrote and signed and mailed to a
foreign land:
"To U.S. Marshal of County Blank, greetings I give to you;
My squad has just brought in your men, and the squad was
Sergeant Blue."

There are things unguessed, there are tales untold, in the
life of the great lone land,
But here is a fact that the prairie-bred alone may under-
stand,
That a thousand miles in the fastnesses the fear of the law
obtains,
And the pioneers of justice were the "Riders of the
Plains".   60

ROBERT STEAD

11

BISHOP HATTO

The summer and autumn had been so wet
That in winter the corn was growing yet;
'Twas a piteous sight to see all around
The grain lie rotting on the ground.

Every day the starving poor
Crowded around Bishop Hatto's door;
For he had a plentiful last-year's store,
And all the neighbourhood could tell
His granaries were furnished well.

At last Bishop Hatto appointed a day   10
To quiet the poor without delay;
He bade them to his great barn repair,
And they should have food for the winter there.

Rejoiced such tidings good to hear,
The poor folk flocked from far and near;
The great barn was full as it could hold,
Of women and children, and young and old.

Then when he saw it could hold no more,
Bishop Hatto he made fast the door;
And while for mercy on Christ they call,   20
He set fire to the barn, and burned them all.

"I' faith, 'tis an excellent bonfire!" quoth he,
"And the country is greatly obliged to me,
For ridding it, in these times forlorn,
Of rats, that only consume the corn."

12

So then to his palace returnèd he,
And he sat down to supper merrily,
And he slept that night like an innocent man;
But Bishop Hatto never slept again.

In the morning as he entered the hall,   **30**
Where his picture hung against the wall,
A sweat like death all over him came,
For the rats had eaten it out of the frame.

As he looked there came a man from the farm;
He had a countenance white with alarm:
"My lord, I opened your granaries this morn,
And the rats had eaten all your corn."

Another came running presently,
And he was pale as pale could be:
"Fly! my Lord Bishop, fly," quoth he,   **40**
"Ten thousand rats are coming this way—
The Lord forgive you for yesterday!"

"I'll go to my tower on the Rhine," replied he,
" 'Tis the safest place in Germany;
The walls are high, and the shores are steep,
And the stream is strong, and the water deep."

Bishop Hatto fearfully hastened away,
And he crossed the Rhine without delay,
And reached his tower, and barred with care
All the windows, doors, and loopholes there.   **50**

He laid him down, and closed his eyes,
But soon a scream made him arise;
He started, and saw two eyes of flame
On his pillow from whence the screaming came.

13

He listened and looked; it was only the cat,
But the Bishop he grew more fearful for that,
For she sat screaming, mad with fear,
At the army of rats that was drawing near.

For they have swum over the river so deep,
And they have climbed the shores so steep,   60
And up the tower their way is bent
To do the work for which they were sent.

They are not to be told by the dozen or score,
By thousands they come, and by myriads and more;
Such numbers had never been heard of before,
Such a judgment had never been witnessed of yore.

Down on his knees the Bishop fell,
And faster and faster his beads did he tell,
As louder and louder drawing near
The gnawing of their teeth he could hear.   70

And in at the windows, and in at the door,
And through the walls helter-skelter they pour,
And down from the ceiling, and up through the floor,
From the right and the left, from behind and before,
From within and without, from above and below,
And all at once to the Bishop they go.

They have whetted their teeth against the stones,
And now they pick the Bishop's bones;
They gnawed the flesh from every limb,
For they were sent to do judgment on him.   80

ROBERT SOUTHEY

14

THE "LAUGHING SALLY"

A wind blew up from Pernambuco.
  (Yeo, heave ho! the *Laughing Sally*,
  Hi yeo, heave away!)
A wind blew out of the east-sou'east
  And boomed at the break of day.

The *Laughing Sally* sped for her life,
  And a speedy craft was she.
The black flag flew at her top to tell
  How she took toll of the sea.

The wind blew up from Pernambuco;
  And in the breast of the blast   **10**
Came the King's black ship, like a hound let slip,
  On the trail of the *Sally* at last.

For a day and a night, a night and a day;
  Over the blue, blue round,
Went on the chase of the pirate quarry,
  The hunt of the tireless hound.

"Land on the port bow!" came the cry,
  And the *Sally* raced for shore,
Till she reached the bar at the river mouth
  Where the shallow breakers roar.   **20**

She passed the bar by a secret channel
  With clear tide under her keel,—
For he knew the shoals like an open book,
  The captain at the wheel.

15

She passed the bar, she sped like a ghost,
  Till her sails were hid from view
By the tall, liana'd, unsunned boughs
  O'erbrooding the dark bayou.

At moonrise up to the river mouth
  Came the King's black ship of war. **30**
The red cross flapped in wrath at her peak,
  But she could not cross the bar.

And while she lay in the run of the seas,
  By the grimmest whim of chance
Out of the bay to the north came forth
  Two battleships of France.

On the English ship the twain bore down
  Like wolves that range by night;
And the breakers' roar was heard no more
  In the thunder of the fight. **40**

The crash of the broadsides rolled and stormed
  To the *Sally* hid from view
Under the tall, liana'd boughs
  Of the moonless, dark bayou.

A boat ran out for news of the fight,
  And this was the word she brought—
"The King's ship fights the ships of France
  As the King's ships all have fought!"

Then muttered the mate, "I'm a man of Devon!"
  And the captain thundered then — **50**
"There's English rope that bides for our necks,
  But we all be English men!"

16

The *Sally* glided out of the gloom
   And down the moon-white river.
She stole like a grey shark over the bar
   Where the long surf seethes for ever.

She hove to under a high French hull,
   And the red cross rose to her peak.
The French were looking for fight that night,
   And they hadn't far to seek.   60

Blood and fire on the streaming decks,
   And fire and blood below;
The heat of hell, and the reek of hell,
   And the dead men laid a-row!

And when the stars paled out of heaven
   And the red dawn-rays uprushed,
The oaths of battle, the crash of timbers,
   The roar of guns was hushed.

With one foe beaten under his bow,
   The other afar in flight   70
The English captain turned to look
   For his fellow in the fight.

The English captain turned, and stared;—
   For where the *Sally* had been
Was a single spar upthrust from the sea
   With the red-cross flag serene!

A wind blew up from Pernambuco,—
   (Yeo, heave ho! the *Laughing Sally*,
   Hi yeo, heave away!)
And boomed the doom of the *Laughing Sally*,
   Gone down at the break of day.   80

SIR CHARLES G. D. ROBERTS

CASEY AT THE BAT

It looked extremely rocky for the Mudville nine that day;
The score stood two to four, with but one inning left to play.
So, when Cooney died at second, and Burrows did the same,
A pallor wreathed the features of the patrons of the game.

A straggling few got up to go, leaving there the rest,
With that hope which springs eternal within the human
breast.
For they thought: "If only Casey could get a whack at that,"
They'd put even money now, with Casey at the bat.

But Flynn preceded Casey, and likewise so did Blake,
And the former was a pudd'n, and the latter was a fake.   10
So on that stricken multitude a deathlike silence sat;
For there seemed but little chance of Casey's getting to the
bat.

But Flynn let drive a single, to the wonderment of all.
And the much-despised Blakey "tore the cover off the ball".
And when the dust had lifted, and they saw what had
occurred,
There was Blakey safe at second, and Flynn a-huggin' third.

Then from the gladdened multitude went up a joyous yell—
It rumbled in the mountain tops, it rattled in the dell;
It struck upon the hillside and rebounded on the flat;
For Casey, mighty Casey, was advancing to the bat.   20

There was ease in Casey's manner as he stepped into his
place,
There was pride in Casey's bearing and a smile on Casey's
face;

And when responding to the cheers he lightly doffed his hat,
No stranger in the crowd could doubt 'twas Casey at the bat.

Ten thousand eyes were on him as he rubbed his hands
with dirt,
Five thousand tongues applauded when he wiped them on
his shirt;
Then when the writhing pitcher ground the ball into his hip,
Defiance glanced in Casey's eye, a sneer curled Casey's lip.

And now the leather-covered sphere came hurtling through
the air,
And Casey stood a-watching it in haughty grandeur there. 30
Close by the sturdy batsman the ball unheeded sped;
"That ain't my style," said Casey. "Strike one," the umpire
said.

From the benches, black with people, there went up a muffled roar,
Like the beating of the storm waves on the stern and distant shore.
"Kill him! kill the umpire!" shouted someone on the stand;
And it's likely they'd have killed him had not Casey raised
his hand.

With a smile of Christian charity great Casey's visage shone;
He stilled the rising tumult, he made the game go on;
He signalled to the pitcher, and once more the spheroid flew,
But Casey still ignored it, and the umpire said, "Strike
two."   40

"Fraud!" cried the maddened thousands, and the echo
answered, "Fraud!"
But one scornful look from Casey, and the audience was
awed;

19

They saw his face grow stern and cold, they saw his muscles strain,
And they knew that Casey wouldn't let the ball go by again.

The sneer is gone from Casey's lips, his teeth are clenched in hate,
He pounds with cruel vengeance his bat upon the plate;
And now the pitcher holds the ball, and now he lets it go,
And now the air is shattered by the force of Casey's blow.

Oh! somewhere in this favoured land the sun is shining bright,
The band is playing somewhere, and somewhere hearts are light; 50
And somewhere men are laughing, and somewhere children shout,
But there is no joy in Mudville—mighty Casey has struck out!

ERNEST LAWRENCE THAYER

JACQUES CARTIER

In the seaport of St. Malo 'twas a smiling morn in May,
When the Commodore Jacques Cartier to the westward sailed away;
In the crowded old cathedral all the town were on their knees
For the safe return of kinsmen from the undiscovered seas;
And every autumn blast that swept o'er pinnacle and pier,
Filled manly hearts with sorrow, and gentle hearts with fear.

A year passed o'er St. Malo—again came round the day
When Commodore Jacques Cartier to the westward sailed away;

But no tidings from the absent had come the way they went,
And tearful were the vigils that many a maiden spent: 10
And manly hearts were filled with gloom, and gentle hearts
    with fear,
When no tidings came from Cartier at the closing of the year.

But the earth is as the future, it hath its hidden side;
And the captain of St. Malo was rejoicing in his pride
In the forests of the north. While his townsmen mourned his
    loss,
He was rearing on Mount Royal the *fleur-de-lis* and cross;
And when two months were over, and added to the year,
St. Malo hailed him home again, cheer answering to cheer.

He told them of a region, hard, iron-bound, and cold,
Nor seas of pearl abounded, nor mines of shining gold;   20
Where the wind from Thulé freezes the word upon the lip,
And the ice in spring comes sailing athwart the early ship;
He told them of the frozen scene until they thrilled with fear,
And piled fresh fuel on the hearth to make him better cheer.

But when he changed the strain—he told how soon are cast
In early spring the fetters that hold the waters fast;
How the winter causeway broken is drifted out to sea,
And the rills and rivers sing with pride the anthem of the
    free;
How the magic wand of summer clad the landscape to his
    eyes,
Like the dry bones of the just when they wake in Paradise. 30

He told them of the Algonquin braves—the hunters of the
    wild,
Of how the Indian mother in the forest rocks her child;
Of how, poor souls, they fancy in every living thing
A spirit good or evil, that claims their worshipping;

Of how they brought their sick and maimed for him to
  breathe upon,
And of the wonders wrought for them through the Gospel
  of St. John.

He told them of the river whose mighty current gave
Its freshness for a hundred leagues to Ocean's briny wave;
He told them of the glorious scene presented to his sight,
What time he reared the cross and crown on Hochelaga's
  height;   40
And of the fortress cliff that keeps of Canada the key,
And they welcomed back Jacques Cartier from his perils
  o'er the sea.

                              THOMAS D'ARCY McGEE

BETH GELERT

The spearmen heard the bugle sound
  And cheerly smiled the morn;
And many a brach and many a hound
  Obeyed Llewelyn's horn.

And still he blew a louder blast
  And gave a lustier cheer;
"Come Gelert, come, wert never last
  Llewelyn's horn to hear.—

"Oh where does faithful Gelert roam,
  The flower of all his race;   10
So true, so brave, a lamb at home,
  A lion in the chase?"

'Twas only at Llewelyn's board
  The faithful Gelert fed;
He watched, he served, he cheered his lord,
  And sentinelled his bed.

In sooth he was a peerless hound,
  The gift of royal John;
But now no Gelert could be found
  And all the chase rode on.   20

And now as o'er the rocks and dells
  The gallant chidings rise,
All Snowdon's craggy chaos yells
  The many-mingled cries!

That day Llewelyn little loved
  The chase of hart and hare;
And scant and small the booty proved,
  Since Gelert was not there.

Unpleased Llewelyn homeward hied,
  When near the portal-seat,   30
His truant Gelert he espied
  Bounding his lord to greet.

But when he gained the castle door
  Aghast the chieftain stood;
The hound all o'er was smeared with gore,
  His lips, his fangs, ran blood.

Llewelyn gazed with fierce surprise;
  Unused such looks to meet,
His favourite checked his joyful guise
  And crouched and licked his feet.   40

23

Onward in haste Llewelyn passed,
    And on went Gelert too;
And still where'er his eyes he cast,
    Fresh blood-gouts shocked his view.

O'erturned his infant's bed he found,
    With blood-stained covert rent;
And all around the walls and ground
    With recent blood besprent.

He called his child—no voice replied—
    He searched with terror wild;   50
Blood, blood, he found on every side,
    But nowhere found his child.

"Hell-hound! my child's by thee devoured,"
    The frantic father cried;
And to the hilt his vengeful sword
    He plunged in Gelert's side.

His suppliant looks as prone he fell
    No pity could impart;
But still his Gelert's dying yell
    Passed heavy o'er his heart.   60

Aroused by Gelert's dying yell
    Some slumberer wakened nigh:—
What words the parent's joy could tell
    To hear his infant's cry!

Concealed beneath a tumbled heap
    His hurried search had missed,
All glowing from his rosy sleep,
    The cherub boy he kissed.

No scath had he, nor harm, nor dread,
   But, the same couch beneath,   **70**
Lay a gaunt wolf all torn and dead,
   Tremendous still in death.

Ah what was then Llewelyn's pain!
   For now the truth was clear;
His gallant hound the wolf had slain
   To save Llewelyn's heir.

Vain, vain was all Llewelyn's woe:
   "Best of thy kind, adieu!
The frantic blow which laid thee low
   This heart shall ever rue."   **80**

And now a handsome tomb they raise,
   With costly sculpture decked;
And marbles storied with his praise,
   Poor Gelert's bones protect.

There never could the spearman pass,
   Or forester, unmoved;
There oft the tear-besprinkled grass
   Llewelyn's sorrow proved.

And there he hung his horn and spear,
   And there as evening fell,   **90**
In fancy's ear he oft would hear
   Poor Gelert's dying yell.

And till great Snowdon's rocks grow old,
   And cease the storm to brave,
The consecrated spot shall hold
   The name of "Gelert's grave".

WILLIAM ROBERT SPENCER

SIR SMASHAM UPPE

Good afternoon, Sir Smasham Uppe!
We're having tea: do take a cup!
Sugar and milk? Now let me see—
Two lumps, I think? . . . Good gracious me!
The silly thing slipped off your knee!
Pray don't apologize, old chap:
A very trivial mishap!
So clumsy of you? How absurd!
My dear Sir Smasham, not a word!
Now do sit down and have another,   10
And tell us all about your brother—
You know, the one who broke his head.
Is the poor fellow still in bed?—
A chair—allow me, sir! . . . Great Scott!
That *was* a nasty smash! Eh, what?
Oh, not at all: the chair was old—
Queen Anne, or so we have been told.
We've got at least a dozen more:
Just leave the pieces on the floor.
I want you to admire our view: 20
Come nearer to the window, do;
And look how beautiful . . . Tut, tut!
You didn't see that it was shut?
I hope you are not badly cut!
Not hurt? A fortunate escape!
Amazing! Not a single scrape!
And now, if you have finished tea,
I fancy you might like to see
A little thing or two I've got.
That china plate? Yes, worth a lot: 30
A beauty too . . . Ah, there it goes!

26

I trust it didn't hurt your toes?
Your elbow brushed it off the shelf?
Of course: I've done the same myself.
And now, my dear Sir Smasham—oh,
You surely don't intend to go?
You *must* be off? Well, come again.
So glad you're fond of porcelain!

E. V. RIEU

THE LITTLE BOATS OF BRITAIN

On many a lazy river, in many a sparkling bay,
The little boats of Britain were dancing, fresh and gay;
The little boats of Britain, by busy wharf and town,
A cheerful battered company, were trading up and down.

A voice of terror through the land ran like a deadly frost:
"King Leopold has left the field,—our men are trapped and
lost.
No battleship can reach the shore, through shallows loud
with foam;
Then who will go to Dunkirk town to bring our armies
home?"

From bustling wharf and lonely bay, from river-side and
coast,
On eager feet came hurrying a strange and motley host,   10
Young lads and grandsires, rich and poor, they breathed one
frantic prayer:
"O send us with our little boats to save our armies there!"

Never did such a motley host put out upon the tide;
The jaunty little pleasure-boats in gaudy, painted pride,

The grimy tugs and fishing-smacks, the tarry hulks of trade,
With paddle, oar, and tattered sail, went forth on their
Crusade.

And on that horror-haunted coast, through roaring bomb
and shell,
Our armies watched around them close the fiery fangs of
hell,
Yet backward, backward to Dunkirk they grimly battled on,
And the brave hearts beat higher still, when hope itself was
gone.   20

And there beneath the bursting skies, amid the mad uproar,
The little boats of Britain were waiting by the shore;
While from the heavens, dark with death, a flaming torrent
fell,
The little boats undaunted lay beside the wharves of hell.

Day after day, night after night, they hurried to and fro;
The screaming planes were loud above, the snarling seas
below,
And haggard men fought hard with sleep, and when their
strength was gone,
Still the brave spirit held them up, and drove them on and on.

And many a grimy little tramp, and skiff of painted pride
Went down in thunder to a grave beneath the bloody tide, 30
But from the horror-haunted coast, across the snarling foam,
The little boats of Britain brought our men in safety home.

Full many a noble vessel sails the shining seas of fame,
And bears, to ages yet to be, an unforgotten name:
The ships that won Trafalgar's fight, that broke the Armada's
pride,—
And the little boats of Britain shall go sailing by their side!

SARA CARSLEY

HOW THEY BROUGHT THE GOOD NEWS

I sprang to the stirrup, and Joris, and he;
I galloped, Dirck galloped, we galloped all three;
"Good speed!" cried the watch, as the gate-bolts un-
  drew;
"Speed!" echoed the wall to us galloping through;
Behind shut the postern, the lights sank to rest,
And into the midnight we galloped abreast.

Not a word to each other; we kept the great pace
Neck by neck, stride by stride, never changing our
  place;
I turned in my saddle and made its girths tight,
Then shortened each stirrup, and set the pique right, 10
Rebuckled the cheek-strap, chained slacker the bit,
Nor galloped less steadily Roland a whit.

'Twas moonset at starting; but while we drew near
Lokeren, the cocks crew and twilight dawned clear;
At Boom, a great yellow star came out to see;
At Düffeld, 'twas morning as plain as could be;
And from Mecheln church-steeple we heard the half-
  chime,
So, Joris broke silence with, "Yet there is time!"

At Aerschot, up leaped of a sudden the sun,
And against him the cattle stood black every one,   20
To stare through the mist at us galloping past,
And I saw my stout galloper Roland at last,
With resolute shoulders, each butting away
The haze, as some bluff river headland its spray:

29

And his low head and crest, just one sharp ear bent
    back
For my voice, and the other pricked out on his track;
And one eye's black intelligence—ever that glance
O'er its white edge at me, his own master, askance!
And the thick heavy spume-flakes which aye and anon
His fierce lips shook upwards in galloping on.   30

By Hasselt, Dirck groaned; and cried Joris, "Stay spur!
Your Roos galloped bravely, the fault's not in her,
We'll remember at Aix"— for one heard the quick
    wheeze
Of her chest, saw the stretched neck and staggering
    knees,
And sunk tail, and horrible heave of the flank,
As down on her haunches she shuddered and sank.

So, we were left galloping, Joris and I,
Past Looz and past Tongres, no cloud in the sky;
The broad sun above laughed a pitiless laugh,
'Neath our feet broke the brittle bright stubble like
    chaff;   40
Till over by Dalhem a dome-spire sprang white,
And "Gallop," gasped Joris, "for Aix is in sight!"

"How they'll greet us!"— and all in a moment his
    roan
Rolled neck and croup over, lay dead as a stone;
And there was my Roland to bear the whole weight
Of the news which alone could save Aix from her fate,
With his nostrils like pits full of blood to the brim,
And with circles of red for his eye-sockets' rim.

Then I cast loose my buffcoat, each holster let fall,
Shook off both my jack-boots, let go belt and all,   50
Stood up in the stirrup, leaned, patted his ear.

Called my Roland his pet-name, my horse without peer;
Clapped my hands, laughed and sang, any noise, bad
   or good,
Till at length into Aix Roland galloped and stood.

And all I remember is friends flocking round
As I sat with his head 'twixt my knees on the ground;
And no voice but was praising this Roland of mine,
As I poured down his throat our last measure of wine,
Which (the burgesses voted by common consent)
Was no more than his due who brought good news
   from Ghent.   **60**

ROBERT BROWNING

THE PRIEST AND THE MULBERRY TREE

Did you hear of the curate who mounted his mare,
And merrily trotted along to the fair?
Of creature more tractable none ever heard:
In the height of her speed she would stop at a word;
But again with a word, when the curate said, "Hey,"
She put forth her mettle and galloped away.

As near to the gates of the city he rode,
While the sun of September all brilliantly glowed,
The good priest discovered, with eyes of desire,
A mulberry tree in a hedge of wild-brier;   **10**
On boughs long and lofty, in many a green shoot,
Hung, large, black and glossy, the beautiful fruit.

The curate was hungry, and thirsty to boot;
He shrank from the thorns, though he longed for the fruit;
With a word he arrested his courser's keen speed,

And he stood up erect on the back of his steed;
On the saddle he stood while the creature stood still,
And he gathered the fruit till he took his good fill.

"Sure never," he thought, "was a creature so rare,
So docile, so true, as my excellent mare: 20
Lo, here now I stand," and he gazed all around,
"As safe and as steady as if on the ground;
Yet how had it been, if some traveller this way
Had, dreaming no mischief, but chanced to cry 'Hey'?"

He stood with his head in the mulberry tree,
And he spoke out aloud in his fond reverie;
At the sound of the word the good mare made a push,
And down went the priest in the wild-brier bush.
He remembered too late, on his thorny green bed,
Much that well may be thought cannot wisely be said.   30

THOMAS LOVE PEACOCK

BONNIE GEORGE CAMPBELL

High upon Highlands,
    And low upon Tay,
Bonnie George Campbell
    Rode out on a day.

Saddled and bridled
    And gallant rode he;
Home came his good horse,
    But never came he.

Out came his old mother,
    Greetin' fu' sair,   10

32

And out came his bonnie bride,
    Rivin' her hair.

"The meadow lies green,
    The corn is unshorn,
But bonnie George Campbell
    Will never return."

Saddled and bridled
    And booted rode he,
A plume in his helmet,
    A sword at his knee.   **20**

But toom came his saddle,
    All bloody to see,
Oh, home came his good horse,
    But never came he.

AUTHOR UNKNOWN

THE CREMATION OF SAM McGEE

There are strange things done in the midnight sun
By the men who moil for gold;
The Arctic trails have their secret tales
That would make your blood run cold;
The Northern Lights have seen queer sights,
But the queerest they ever did see
Was that night on the marge of Lake Lebarge
I cremated Sam McGee.

Now Sam McGee was from Tennessee, where the cotton
    blooms and blows.
Why he left his home in the South to roam 'round the Pole,
    God only knows.   **10**

33

He was always cold, but the land of gold seemed to hold him
    like a spell;
Though he'd often say in his homely way that "he'd sooner
    live in hell."

On a Christmas day we were mushing our way over the
    Dawson trail.
Talk of your cold! through the parka's fold it stabbed like
    a driven nail.
If our eyes we'd close, then the lashes froze till sometimes
    we couldn't see;
It wasn't much fun, but the only one to whimper was Sam
    McGee.

And that very night, as we lay packed tight in our robes
    beneath the snow,
And the dogs were fed, and the stars o'erhead were dancing
    heel and toe,
He turned to me, and "Cap," says he, "I'll cash in this trip,
    I guess;
And if I do, I'm asking that you won't refuse my last
    request."   **20**

Well, he seemed so low that I couldn't say no; then he says
    with a sort of moan:
"It's the cursed cold, and it's got right hold till I'm chilled
    clean through to the bone.
Yet 'tain't being dead—it's my awful dread of the icy grave
    that pains;
So I want you to swear that, foul or fair, you'll cremate my
    last remains."

A pal's last need is a thing to heed, so I swore I would not
    fail;
And so we started on at streak of dawn; but God! he looked
    ghastly pale.

He crouched on the sleigh, and he raved all day of his home
  in Tennessee;
And before nightfall a corpse was all that was left of Sam
  McGee.

There wasn't a breath in that land of death, and I hurried,
  horror-driven,
With a corpse half-hid that I couldn't get rid, because of a
  promise given;   30
It was lashed to the sleigh, and it seemed to say: "You may
  tax your brawn and brains,
But you promised true, and it's up to you to cremate these
  last remains."

Now a promise made is a debt unpaid, and the trail has its
  own stern code.
In the days to come, though my lips were dumb, in my heart
  how I cursed that load.
In the long, long night, by the lone fire-light, while the
  huskies, round in a ring,
Howled out their woes to the homeless snows—O God!
  how I loathed the thing!

And every day that quiet clay seemed to heavy and heavier
  grow;
And on I went, though the dogs were spent and the grub
  was getting low;
The trail was bad, and I felt half mad, but I swore I wouldn't
  give in;
And I'd often sing to the hateful thing, and it hearkened
  with a grin.   40

Till I came to the marge of Lake Lebarge, and a derelict
  there lay;
It was jammed in the ice, and I saw in a trice it was called
  the *Alice May*.

And I looked at it, and I thought a bit, and I looked at my
frozen chum;
Then "Here," said I, with a sudden cry, "is my cre-ma-
tor-eum."

Some planks I tore from the cabin floor, and I lit the boiler
fire;
Some coal I found that was lying around, and I heaped the
fuel higher;
The flames just soared, and the furnace roared—such a blaze
you seldom see;
And I burrowed a hole in the glowing coal, and I stuffed in
Sam McGee.

Then I made a hike, for I didn't like to hear him sizzle so;
And the heavens scowled, and the huskies howled, and the
wind began to blow.   50
It was icy cold, but the hot sweat rolled down my cheeks,
and I don't know why;
And the greasy smoke in an inky cloak went streaking down
the sky.

I do not know how long in the snow I wrestled with grisly
fear;
But the stars came out and they danced about ere again I
ventured near;
I was sick with dread, but I bravely said: "I'll just take a
peep inside.
I guess he's cooked, and it's time I looked;" . . . then the
door I opened wide.

And there sat Sam, looking cool and calm, in the heart of
the furnace roar;
And he wore a smile you could see a mile, and he said:
"Please close that door.

36

It's fine in here, but I greatly fear you'll let in the cold and
    storm—
Since I left Plumtree, down in Tennessee, it's the first time
    I've been warm."   **60**

There are strange things done in the midnight sun
By the men who moil for gold;
The Arctic trails have their secret tales
That would make your blood run cold;
The Northern Lights have seen queer sights,
But the queerest they ever did see
Was that night on the marge of Lake Lebarge
I cremated Sam McGee.

ROBERT W. SERVICE

THE GLOVE AND THE LIONS

King Francis was a hearty king, and loved a royal sport,
And one day, as his lions fought, sat looking on the court.
The nobles filled the benches, with ladies in their pride,
And 'mongst them sat the Count de Lorge, with one for
    whom he sighed:
And truly 'twas a gallant thing to see the crowning show,
Valour and love, and a king above, and the royal beasts
    below.

Ramped and roared the lions, with horrid laughing jaws;
They bit, they glared, gave blows like beams, a wind went
    with their paws,
With wallowing might and stifled roar they rolled on one
    another,
Till all the pit with sand and mane was in a thunderous
    smother;   **10**

The bloody foam above the bars came whisking through the
  air;
Said Francis then, "Faith, gentlemen, we're better here than
  there."

De Lorge's love o'erheard the king, a beauteous, lively dame,
With smiling lips and sharp bright eyes, which always
  seemed the same;
She thought: "The Count, my lover, is brave as brave can be;
He surely would do wondrous things to show his love of me.
King, ladies, lovers, all look on; the occasion is divine.
I'll drop my glove, to prove his love; great glory will be
  mine."

She dropped her glove, to prove his love, then looked at him
  and smiled;
He bowed, and in a moment leaped among the lions wild: 20
The leap was quick, return was quick, he has regained his
  place,
Then threw the glove, but not with love, right in the lady's
  face.
"By heaven," said Francis, "rightly done!" and he rose from
  where he sat;
"No love," quoth he, "but vanity, sets love a task like that."

LEIGH HUNT

KING JOHN AND THE ABBOT OF
CANTERBURY

An ancient story I'll tell you anon,
Of a notable prince, that was called King John;
He ruled over England with main and might,
But he did great wrong, and maintained little right.

38

And I'll tell you a story, a story so merry,
Concerning the Abbot of Canterbury;
How for his housekeeping and high renown,
They rode post to bring him to London town.

A hundred men, as the King heard say,
The Abbot kept in his house every day;   10
And fifty gold chains, without any doubt,
In velvet coats waited the Abbot about.

"How now, Father Abbot? I hear it of thee,
Thou keepest a far better house than me;
And for thy housekeeping and high renown,
I fear thou work'st treason against my crown."

"My Liege," quoth the Abbot, "I would it were known,
I am spending nothing but what is my own;
And I trust your Grace will not put me in fear,
For spending my own true-gotten gear."   20

"Yes, yes, Father Abbot, thy fault is high,
And now for the same thou needs must die;
And except thou canst answer me questions three,
Thy head struck off from thy body shall be.

"Now first," quoth the King, "as I sit here,
With my crown of gold on my head so fair,
Among all my liegemen of noble birth,
Thou must tell to one penny what I am worth.

"Secondly, tell me, beyond all doubt,
How quickly I may ride the whole world about;   30
And at the third question thou must not shrink,
But tell me here truly, what do I think?"

"Oh, these are deep questions for my shallow wit,
And I cannot answer your Grace as yet;

39

But if you will give me a fortnight's space,
I'll do my endeavour to answer your Grace."

"Now a fortnight's space to thee will I give,
And that is the longest thou hast to live;
For unless thou answer my questions three,
Thy life and thy lands are forfeit to me."   40

Away rode the Abbot all sad at this word;
He rode to Cambridge and Oxenford;
But never a doctor there was so wise,
That could by his learning an answer devise.

Then home rode the Abbot, with comfort so cold,
And he met his shepherd, a-going to fold:
"Now, good Lord Abbot, you are welcome home;
What news do you bring us from great King John?"

"Sad news, sad news, Shepherd, I must give;
That I have but three days more to live.   50
I must answer the King his questions three,
Or my head struck off from my body shall be.

"The first is to tell him, as he sits there,
With his crown of gold on his head so fair
Among all his liegemen of noble birth,
To within one penny, what he is worth.

"The second, to tell him, beyond all doubt,
How quickly he may ride this whole world about;
And at question the third I must not shrink,
But tell him there truly, what does he think?"   60

"Oh, cheer up, my lord; did you never hear yet
That a fool may teach a wise man wit?
Lend me your serving-men, horse, and apparel,
And I'll ride to London to answer your quarrel.

"With your pardon, it oft has been told to me
That I'm like your lordship as ever can be:
And if you will but lend me your gown,
There is none shall know us at London town."

"Now horses and serving-men thou shalt have,
With sumptuous raiment gallant and brave;   70
With crozier, and mitre, and rochet, and cope,
Fit to draw near to our father, the pope."

"Now welcome, Sir Abbot," the King he did say,
" 'Tis well thou'rt come back to keep thy day;
For if thou canst answer my questions three,
Thy life and thy living both saved shall be.

"And first, as thou seest me sitting here,
With my crown of gold on my head so fair,
Among my liegemen of noble birth,
Tell to one penny what I am worth."   80

"For thirty pence our Saviour was sold
Among the false Jews as I have been told;
And twenty-nine is the worth of thee;
For I think thou art one penny worse than he."

The King, he laughed, and swore by St. Bittle,
"I did not think I was worth so little!
Now secondly tell me, beyond all doubt,
How quickly I may ride this world about."

"You must rise with the sun, and ride with the same,
Until the next morning he riseth again;   90
And then your Grace need never doubt
But in twenty-four hours you'll ride it about."

The King he laughed, and swore by St. Jone,
"I did not think I could do it so soon!

Now from question the third thou must not shrink,
But tell me truly, what do I think?"

"Yea, that I shall do, and make your Grace merry:
You think I'm the Abbot of Canterbury.
But I'm his poor shepherd, as plain you may see,
That am come to beg pardon for him and for me." **100**

The King he laughed, and swore by the mass,
"I'll make thee Lord Abbot this day in his place!"
"Now nay, my Liege, be not in such speed;
For alas! I can neither write nor read."

"Four nobles a week, then I'll give to thee,
For this merry jest thou hast shown to me;
And tell the old Abbot, when thou gettest home,
Thou hast brought a free pardon with thanks from
  King John."

AUTHOR UNKNOWN

JOHNNY APPLESEED

"Orchards," said Johnny Appleseed,
"Let there be orchards, yes, indeed,
Orchards, orchards, everywhere,
I've got these orchards in my hair,
Orchards to bloom, orchards to bear,
And apple trees
To scent the breeze
In blossom time."

And so he tramped from east to west
Planting seeds with zeal and zest, **10**

He sowed them here, he sowed them there,
He planted apples everywhere.
He had no place to lay his head,
He could not earn his daily bread,
The sky the only roof he had
And yet his simple heart was glad
For he was doing what he knew
Life had taught him best to do;
And he could lay him down at night,
The stars his only candle-light,   20
And watch them travel who knows where
Or were they growing in the air,
The same as seeds that he had scattered,
Then fall asleep, for nothing mattered.
His clothes were threadbare, full of holes,
His shoes were sadly lacking soles,
Upon his head an old tin pan
And people said, "There goes a man
Who talks with animals and birds,
He seems to know their very words."   30
And he could tell about the weather,
His face was tanned as saddle leather,
And little children loved his stories
Of apple trees and morning glories;
Of centipedes and blowing whales,
Of Indians he'd tell tall tales,
And they would gather at his knee
And wonder what the yarn would be.
When he came by no dogs did bark,
Something he had, a friendly spark   40
That miracles worked, and when he laughed
Dogs wagged their tails and people chaffed.

The apple seeds that he would sow
They couldn't help but prosper, grow,

And apple trees sprang far and near
To show that Johnny had been here.
"His witness trees," he said with pride,
"You'll find them 'cross the country-side."
And settlers clearing near a glade
At noon would lie beneath the shade   50
Of apple trees that he had planted,
And take it more or less for granted,
Enjoy a friendly, homelike feeling
Thinking of days back east when stealing
Apples was but boyish fun
And rise refreshed for work begun.
And so it went from year to year
Till Appleseed was in the sear
And dawned the day that he must die.
He laid him down beneath the sky   60
Within an orchard of his trees.
In blossom time, on every breeze
The fragrance of the bloom was blown,
The very bloom that he had sown,
His broken helmet on the grass,
The warrior is home at last.
Some apple seeds lay at his side,
He scattered them before he died.
They did not move him from the spot,
For him no cemetery plot,   70
He loved the fellowship of trees,
The gnarled roots touched gnarled knees,
A winding sheet of barrel staves
That had held apples all their days.
And so he chose his place of rest,
An orchard, for he loved it best.

"Orchards," said Johnny Appleseed,
"Let there be orchards, yes, indeed,

44

Orchards, orchards, everywhere,
I've got these orchards in my hair,   80
Orchards to bloom, orchards to bear,
And apple trees
To scent the breeze
In blossom time."

ARTHUR STANLEY BOURINOT

THE WALRUS AND THE CARPENTER

The sun was shining on the sea,
   Shining with all his might:
He did his very best to make
   The billows smooth and bright—
And this was odd, because it was
   The middle of the night.

The moon was shining sulkily,
   Because she thought the sun
Had got no business to be there
   After the day was done—   10
"It's very rude of him," she said,
   "To come and spoil the fun!"

The sea was wet as wet could be,
   The sands were dry as dry.
You could not see a cloud, because
   No cloud was in the sky:
No birds were flying overhead—
   There were no birds to fly.

The Walrus and the Carpenter
   Were walking close at hand;   20

45

They wept like anything to see
   Such quantities of sand.
"If this were only cleared away,"
   They said, "it *would* be grand!"

"If seven maids with seven mops
   Swept it for half a year,
Do you suppose," the Walrus said,
   "That they could get it clear?"
"I doubt it," said the Carpenter,
   And shed a bitter tear.   30

"O Oysters, come and walk with us!"
   The Walrus did beseech.
"A pleasant walk, a pleasant talk,
   Along the briny beach:
We cannot do with more than four,
   To give a hand to each."

The eldest Oyster looked at him,
   But never a word he said:
The eldest Oyster winked his eye,
   And shook his heavy head—   40
Meaning to say he did not choose
   To leave the oyster-bed.

But four young Oysters hurried up,
   All eager for the treat:
Their coats were brushed, their faces washed,
   Their shoes were clean and neat—
And this was odd, because, you know,
   They hadn't any feet.

Four other Oysters followed them,
   And yet another four;   50
And thick and fast they came at last,

And more, and more, and more—
All hopping through the frothy waves,
  And scrambling to the shore.

The Walrus and the Carpenter
  Walked on a mile or so,
And then they rested on a rock
  Conveniently low;
And all the little Oysters stood
  And waited in a row.   60

"The time has come," the Walrus said,
  "To talk of many things:
Of shoes and ships and sealing-wax,
  Of cabbages and kings;
And why the sea is boiling hot—
  And whether pigs have wings."

"But wait a bit," the Oysters cried,
  "Before we have our chat;
For some of us are out of breath,
  And all of us are fat!"   70
"No hurry!" said the Carpenter.
  They thanked him much for that.

"A loaf of bread," the Walrus said,
  "Is what we chiefly need:
Pepper and vinegar, besides,
  Are very good indeed—
Now, if you're ready, Oysters dear,
  We can begin to feed."

"But not on us!" the Oysters cried,
  Turning a little blue.   80
"After such kindness, that would be
  A dismal thing to do!"

47

"The night is fine," the Walrus said.
  "Do you admire the view?

"It was so kind of you to come!
  And you are very nice!"
The Carpenter said nothing but
  "Cut us another slice;
I wish you were not quite so deaf—
  I've had to ask you twice!"   **90**

"It seems a shame," the Walrus said,
  "To play them such a trick,
After we've brought them out so far,
  And made them trot so quick!"
The Carpenter said nothing but
  "The butter's spread too thick!"

"I weep for you," the Walrus said:
  "I deeply sympathize."
With sobs and tears he sorted out
  Those of the largest size,   **100**
Holding his pocket-handkerchief
  Before his streaming eyes.

"O Oysters," said the Carpenter,
  "You've had a pleasant run!
Shall we be trotting home again?"
  But answer came there none—
And this was scarcely odd, because
  They'd eaten every one.

LEWIS CARROLL

THE ADMIRAL'S GHOST

I tell you a tale tonight
    Which a seaman told to me,
With eyes that gleamed in the lanthorn light
    And a voice as low as the sea.

You could almost hear the stars
    Twinkling up in the sky,
And the old wind woke and moaned in the spars,
    And the same old waves went by,

Singing the same old song
    As ages and ages ago,   10
While he froze my blood in that deep-sea night
    With the things that he seemed to know.

A bare foot pattered on deck;
    Ropes creaked—then all grew still,
And he pointed his finger straight in my face
    And growled, as a sea-dog will.

"Do 'ee know who Nelson was?
    That pore little shrivelled form
With the patch on his eye, and the pinned-up sleeve
    And a soul like a North Sea storm?   20

"Ask of the Devonshire men!
    They know, and they'll tell you true;
He wasn't the pore little chawed-up chap
    That Hardy thought he knew.

"He wasn't the man you think!
    His patch was a dern disguise!

49

For he knew that they'd find him out, d'you see,
  If they looked him in both his eyes.

"He was twice as big as he seemed;
  But his clothes were cunningly made,   30
He'd both of his hairy arms all right!
  The sleeve was a trick of the trade.

"You've heard of sperrits, no doubt;
  Well, there's more in the matter than that!
But he wasn't the patch and he wasn't the sleeve,
  And he wasn't the lace cocked hat.

"*Nelson was just—a ghost!*
  You may laugh! But the Devonshire men
They knew that he'd come when England called,
  And they know that he'll come again.   40

"I'll tell you the way it was
  (For none of the landsmen know),
And to tell it you right, you must go astarn
  Two hundred years or so.

"The waves were lapping and slapping
  The same as they are today;
And Drake lay dying aboard his ship
  In Nombre Dios Bay.

"The scent of the foreign flowers
  Came floating all around;   50
'But I'd give my soul for the smell o' the pitch,'
  Says he, 'in Plymouth Sound.

" 'What shall I do,' he says,
  'When the guns begin to roar,
An' England wants me, and me not there
  To shatter 'er foes once more?'

50

"(You've heard what he said, maybe,
   But I'll mark you the points again;
For I want you to box your compass right
   And get my story plain.)   60

" 'You must take my drum,' he says,
   'To the old sea-wall at home;
And if ever you strike that drum,' he says,
   'Why, strike me blind, I'll come!

" 'If England needs me, dead
   Or living, I'll rise that day!
I'll rise from the darkness under the sea
   Ten thousand miles away.'

"That's what he said; and he died;
   An' his pirates listenin' roun',   70
With their crimson doublets and jewelled swords
   That flashed as the sun went down,

"They sewed him up in his shroud
   With a round shot top and toe,
To sink him under the salt sharp sea
   Where all good seamen go.

"They lowered him down in the deep,
   And there in the sunset light
They boomed a broadside over his grave,
   As meanin' to say, 'Good-night'.   80

"They sailed away in the dark
   To the dear little isle they knew;
And they hung his drum by the old sea-wall
   The same as he told them to.

"Two hundred years went by,
   And the guns began to roar,

51

And England was fighting hard for her life,
  As ever she fought of yore.

" 'It's only my dead that count,'
  She said, as she says today;   90
'It isn't the ships and it isn't the guns
  'Ull sweep Trafalgar's Bay.'

"D'you guess who Nelson was?
  You may laugh, but it's true as true!
There was more in that pore little chawed-up chap
  Than ever his best friend knew.

"The foe was creepin' close,
  In the dark to our white-cliffed isle;
They were ready to leap at England's throat
  When—Oh, you may smile, you may smile;   100

"But—ask of the Devonshire men;
  For they heard in the dead of night
The roll of a drum, and they saw *him* pass
  On a ship all shining white.

"He stretched out his dead cold face
  And he sailed in the grand old way!
The fishes had taken an eye and an arm,
  But he swept Trafalgar's Bay.

"Nelson—was Francis Drake!
  Oh, what matters the uniform,   110
Or the patch on your eye or your pinned-up sleeve,
  If your soul's like a North Sea storm?"

ALFRED NOYES

52

THE WHITE SHIP

By none but me can the tale be told,
The butcher of Rouen, poor Berold.
    (*Lands are swayed by a king on a throne.*)
'Twas a royal train put forth to sea,
Yet the tale can be told by none but me.
    (*The sea hath no king but God alone.*)

King Henry held it as life's whole gain
That after his death his son should reign.

'Twas so in my youth I heard men say
And my old age calls it back today.   **10**

King Henry of England's realm was he,
And Henry Duke of Normandy.

Of ruthless strokes full many a one
He struck to crown himself and his son.

But all the chiefs of the English land
Had knelt and kissed the Prince's hand.

And next with his son he sailed to France
To claim the Norman allegiance.

And every baron in Normandy
Had taken the oath of fealty.   **20**

'Twas sworn and sealed, and the day had come
When the King and the Prince might journey
    home.

For Christmas cheer is to home hearts dear,
And Christmas now was drawing near.

The King set sail with the eve's south wind,
And soon he left that coast behind.

The Prince and all his, a princely show,
Remained in the good White Ship to go.

With noble knights and with ladies fair,
With courtiers and sailors gathered there,   30
Three hundred living souls we were.

And I, Berold, was the meanest hind
In all that train to the Prince assigned.

And now he cried, "Bring wine from below;
Let the sailors revel ere they row;

Our speed shall o'ertake my father's flight
Though we sail from the harbour at midnight."

The rowers made good cheer without check;
The lords and ladies obeyed his beck;
The night was light, and they danced on the
    deck.   40

But at midnight's stroke they cleared the bay,
And the White Ship furrowed the water-way.

The sails were set, and the oars kept tune
To the double flight of the ship and the moon.

Swifter and swifter the White Ship sped
Till she flew as the spirit flies from the dead:

As white as a lily glimmered she
Like a ship's fair ghost upon the sea.

And the Prince cried, "Friends, 'tis the hour to
    sing!
Is the song-bird's course as swift on the wing?" 50

And under the winter stars' still throng,
From brown throats, white throats, merry and
   strong,
The knights and ladies raised a song.

A song—nay, a shriek that rent the sky,
That leaped o'er the deep!—the grievous cry
Of three hundred living that now must die.

An instant shriek that sprang to the shock
As the ship's keel felt the sunken rock.

'Tis said that afar—a shrill strange sigh—
The King's ships heard it and knew not why.   **60**

Pale Fitz-Stephen stood by the helm
'Mid all those folk that the waves must whelm.

A great king's heir for the waves to whelm,
And the helpless pilot pale at the helm!

The ship was eager and sucked athirst,
By the stealthy stab of the sharp reef pierced.

And like the moil round a sinking cup
The waters against her crowded up.

A moment the pilot's senses spin—
The next he snatched the Prince 'mid the din,   **70**
Cut the boat loose, and the youth leaped in.

A few friends leaped with him, standing near.
"Row! the sea's smooth and the night is clear!"

"What! none to be saved but these and I?"
"Row, row as you'd live! All here must die!"

Out of the churn of the choking ship,
Which the gulf grapples and the waves strip,
They struck with the strained oars' flash and dip.

'Twas then o'er the splitting bulwarks' brim
The Prince's sister screamed to him.   80

He gazed aloft, still rowing apace,
And through the whirled surf he knew her face.

To the toppling deck clove one and all
As a fly cleaves to a chamber-wall.

I, Berold, was clinging anear;
I prayed for myself and quaked with fear,
But I saw his eyes as he looked at her.

He knew her face and he heard her cry,
And he said, "Put back! she must not die!"

And back with the current's force they reel   90
Like a leaf that's drawn to a water-wheel.

'Neath the ship's travail they scarce might float,
But he rose and stood in the rocking boat.

Low the poor ship leaned on the tide.
O'er the naked keel as she best might slide.
The sister toiled to the brother's side.

He reached an oar to her from below,
And stiffened his arms to clutch her so.

But now from the ship some spied the boat,
And "Saved!" was the cry from many a throat.   100

And down to the boat they leaped and fell:
It turned as a bucket turns in a well,
And nothing was there but the surge and the
    swell.

The Prince that was and the King to come,
There in an instant gone to his doom,

Despite of all England's bended knee
And maugre the Norman fealty!

He was a prince of lust and pride;
He showed no grace till the hour he died.

When he should be king, he oft would vow,   110
He'd yoke the peasant to his own plough.
O'er him the ships score their furrows now.

God only knows where his soul did wake,
But I saw him die for his sister's sake.

By none but me can the tale be told,
The butcher of Rouen, poor Berold.
(*Lands are swayed by a king on a throne.*)
'Twas a royal train put forth to sea,
Yet the tale can be told by none but me.
    (*The sea hath no king but God alone.*)   120

DANTE GABRIEL ROSSETTI

THE PIED PIPER OF HAMELIN

Hamelin town's in Brunswick,
  By famous Hanover city;
The river Weser, deep and wide,
Washes its wall on the southern side;
A pleasanter spot you never spied;
  But, when begins my ditty,
Almost five hundred years ago,
To see the townsfolk suffer so
  From vermin, was a pity.

Rats!
They fought the dogs and killed the cats,
   And bit the babies in the cradles,
And ate the cheeses out of the vats,
   And licked the soup from the cooks' own ladles,
Split open the kegs of salted sprats,
Made nests inside men's Sunday hats,
And even spoiled the women's chats,
   By drowning their speaking
   With shrieking and squeaking
In fifty different sharps and flats.

At last the people in a body
   To the Town Hall came flocking:
" 'Tis clear," cried they, "our Mayor's a noddy;
And as for our Corporation—shocking
To think we buy gowns lined with ermine
For dolts that can't or won't determine
What's best to rid us of our vermin!
You hope, because you're old and obese,
To find in the furry civic robe ease?
Rouse up, sirs! Give your brains a racking
To find the remedy we're lacking,
Or, sure as fate, we'll send you packing!"
At this the Mayor and Corporation
Quaked with a mighty consternation.

An hour they sat in council;
At length the Mayor broke silence:
"For a guilder I'd my ermine gown sell;
I wish I were a mile hence!
It's easy to bid one rack one's brain—
I'm sure my poor head aches again,
I've scratched it so, and all in vain.
Oh, for a trap, a trap, a trap!"
Just as he said this, what should hap,

At the chamber door, but a gentle tap.
"Bless us!" cried the Mayor, "what's that?"
(With the Corporation as he sat,
Looking little though wondrous fat;
Nor brighter was his eye, nor moister
Than a too-long-opened oyster,
Save when at noon his paunch grew mutinous   50
For a plate of turtle, green and glutinous.)
"Only a scraping of shoes on the mat!
Anything like the sound of a rat
Makes my heart go pit-a-pat!"

"Come in!" the Mayor cried, looking bigger,
And in did come the strangest figure!
His queer long coat, from heel to head,
Was half of yellow and half of red;
And he himself was tall and thin,
With sharp blue eyes, each like a pin,   60
And light loose hair, yet swarthy skin,
No tuft on cheek nor beard on chin,
But lips where smiles went out and in;
There was no guessing his kith and kin.
And nobody could enough admire
The tall man and his quaint attire.
Quoth one: "It's as if my great grandsire,
Starting up at the Trump of Doom's tone,
Had walked this way from his painted tombstone!"

He advanced to the council-table: 70
And, "Please your honours," said he, "I'm able,
By means of a secret charm, to draw
All creatures living beneath the sun
That creep, or swim, or fly, or run,
After me so as you never saw!
And I chiefly use my charm
On creatures that do people harm—

The mole, the toad, the newt, the viper;
And people call me the Pied Piper."
(And here they noticed round his neck   80
A scarf of red and yellow stripe,
To match his coat of the self-same cheque,
And at the scarf's end hung a pipe;
And his fingers, they noticed, were ever straying
As if impatient to be playing
Upon this pipe, as low it dangled
Over his vesture so old-fangled.)
"Yet," said he, "poor piper as I am,
In Tartary I freed the Cham,
Last June, from his huge swarms of gnats;   90
I eased in Asia the Nizam
Of a monstrous brood of vampire bats;
And, as for what your brain bewilders,
If I can rid your town of rats
Will you give me a thousand guilders?"
"One? fifty thousand!" was the exclamation
Of the astonished Mayor and Corporation.

Into the street the Piper stept,
    Smiling first a little smile,
As if he knew what magic slept   100
    In his quiet pipe the while;
Then, like a musical adept,
To blow the pipe his lips he wrinkled,
And green and blue his sharp eyes twinkled,
Like a candle-flame where salt is sprinkled;
And ere three shrill notes the pipe uttered,
You heard as if an army muttered;
And the muttering grew to a grumbling;
And the grumbling grew to a mighty rumbling;
And out of the houses the rats came tumbling.   110
Great rats, small rats, lean rats, brawny rats,

Brown rats, black rats, grey rats, tawny rats,
Grave old plodders, gay young friskers,
  Fathers, mothers, uncles, cousins,
Cocking tails, and pricking whiskers,
  Families by tens and dozens,
Brothers, sisters, husbands, wives—
Followed the Piper for their lives.
From street to street he piped advancing,
And step for step they followed dancing,   120
Until they came to the river Weser,
Wherein all plunged and perished!
—Save one, who, stout as Julius Caesar,
Swam across and lived to carry
(As he, the manuscript he cherished)
To Rat-land home his commentary:
Which was, "At the first shrill notes of the pipe
I heard a sound as of scraping tripe,
And putting apples, wondrous ripe,
Into a cider-press's gripe: 130
And a moving away of pickle-tub boards,
And a leaving ajar of conserve cupboards,
And a drawing the corks of train-oil flasks,
And a breaking the hoops of butter-casks;
And it seemed as if a voice
(Sweeter far than by harp or by psaltery
Is breathed) called out, 'Oh, rats, rejoice!
The world is grown to one vast drysaltery!
So munch on, crunch on, take your nuncheon,
Breakfast, dinner, supper, luncheon!'   140
And just as a bulky sugar-puncheon,
All ready staved, like a great sun shone
Glorious, scarce an inch before me,
Just as methought it said, 'Come, bore me!'
—I found the Weser rolling o'er me."

61

You should have heard the Hamelin people
Ringing the bells till they rocked the steeple.
"Go," cried the Mayor, "and get long poles,
Poke out the nests, and block up the holes!
Consult with carpenters and builders,　　　150
And leave in our town not even a trace
Of the rats!"—when suddenly, up the face
Of the Piper perked in the market-place,
With a, "First, if you please, my thousand guilders!"

A thousand guilders! The Mayor looked blue;
So did the Corporation, too.
For council dinners made rare havoc
With Claret, Moselle, Vin-de-Grave, Hock;
And half the money would replenish
Their cellar's biggest butt with Rhenish.　　　160
To pay this sum to a wandering fellow
With a gipsy coat of red and yellow!
"Beside," quoth the Mayor, with a knowing wink,
"Our business was done at the river's brink;
We saw with our eyes the vermin sink,
And what's dead can't come to life, I think.
So, friend, we're not the folks to shrink
From the duty of giving you something for drink,
And a matter of money to put in your poke;
But, as for the guilders, what we spoke　　　170
Of them, as you very well know, was in joke.
Beside, our losses have made us thrifty.
A thousand guilders! Come, take fifty!"

The Piper's face fell, and he cried,
"No trifling! I can't wait, beside!
I've promised to visit by dinner-time
Bagdat, and accept the prime
Of the head cook's pottage, all he's rich in,
For having left, in the Caliph's kitchen,

Of a nest of scorpions no survivor.   180
With him I proved no bargain-driver;
With you, don't think I'll bate a stiver!
And folks who put me in a passion
May find me pipe to another fashion."

"How?" cried the Mayor, "d'ye think I'll brook
Being worse treated than a cook?
Insulted by a lazy ribald
With idle pipe and vesture piebald?
You threaten us, fellow? Do your worst!
Blow your pipe there till you burst!"   190

Once more he stept into the street,
    And to his lips again
Laid his long pipe of smooth, straight cane;
    And ere he blew three notes (such sweet,
Soft notes as yet musician's cunning
    Never gave the enraptured air)
There was a rustling that seemed like a bustling
Of merry crowds justling at pitching and hustling;
Small feet were pattering, wooden shoes clattering,
Little hands clapping and little tongues chattering, 200
And, like fowls in a farmyard when barley is
    scattering,
    Out came the children running.
    All the little boys and girls,
    With rosy cheeks and flaxen curls,
    And sparkling eyes and teeth like pearls,
Tripping and skipping, ran merrily after
The wonderful music with shouting and laughter.

The Mayor was dumb, and the Council stood
As if they were changed into blocks of wood,
Unable to move a step, or cry   210
To the children merrily skipping by,

63

—And could only follow with the eye
That joyous crowd at the Piper's back.
But how the Mayor was on the rack,
And the wretched Council's bosoms beat,
As the Piper turned from the High Street
To where the Weser rolled its waters
Right in the way of their sons and daughters!
However, he turned from South to West,
And to Koppelberg Hill his steps addressed,   220
And after him the children pressed;
Great was the joy in every breast.
"He never can cross that mighty top!
He's forced to let the piping drop,
And we shall see our children stop!"
When, lo, as they reached the mountain-side,
A wondrous portal opened wide,
As if a cavern was suddenly hollowed;
And the Piper advanced, and the children followed,
And when all were in to the very last,   230
The door in the mountain-side shut fast.
Did I say all? No! One was lame,
And could not dance the whole of the way;
And in after years, if you would blame
His sadness, he was used to say—
"It's dull in our town since my playmates left!
I can't forget that I'm bereft
Of all the pleasant sights they see,
Which the Piper also promised me.
For he led us, he said, to a joyous land,   240
Joining the town and just at hand,
Where waters gushed and fruit trees grew,
And flowers put forth a fairer hue,
And everything was strange and new;
The sparrows were brighter than peacocks here,
And their dogs outran our fallow-deer,

And honey-bees had lost their stings,
And horses were born with eagles' wings;
And just as I became assured
My lame foot would be speedily cured,   250
The music stopped, and I stood still,
And found myself outside the hill,
Left alone against my will,
To go now limping as before,
And never hear of that country more!"

Alas, alas for Hamelin!
   There came into many a burgher's pate
   A text which says that heaven's gate
   Opes to the rich at as easy rate
As the needle's eye takes a camel in!   260

The Mayor sent East, West, North, and South,
To offer the Piper, by word of mouth,
   Wherever it was men's lot to find him,
Silver and gold to his heart's content,
If he'd only return the way he went,
   And bring the children behind him.
But when they saw 'twas a lost endeavour,
And Piper and dancers were gone forever,
They made a decree that lawyers never
   Should think their records dated duly   270
If, after the day of the month and the year,
These words did not as well appear:
"And so long after what happened here
   On the twenty-second of July,
Thirteen hundred and seventy-six";
And the better in memory to fix
The place of the children's last retreat,
They called it the Pied Piper's Street—
Where anyone playing on pipe or tabor

Was sure for the future to lose his labour.   **280**
Nor suffered they hostelry or tavern
   To shock with mirth a street so solemn;
But opposite the place of the cavern
   They wrote the story on a column,
And on the great church-window painted
The same, to make the world acquainted
How their children were stolen away;
And there it stands to this very day.
And I must not omit to say
That in Transylvania there's a tribe   **290**
Of alien people that ascribe
Their outlandish ways and dress,
On which their neighbours lay such stress,
To their fathers and mothers having risen
Out of some subterranean prison
Into which they were trepanned,
Long time ago in a mighty band,
Out of Hamelin town in Brunswick land,
But how or why, they don't understand.

So, Willy, let you and me be wipers   **300**
Of scores out with all men—especially pipers!
And, whether they pipe us free from rats or from
    mice,
If we've promised them aught, let us keep our
    promise!

                            ROBERT BROWNING

THE "REVENGE"

At Flores in the Azores Sir Richard Grenville lay,
And a pinnace, like a fluttered bird, came flying from far
    away:
"Spanish ships of war at sea! we have sighted fifty-three!"
Then sware Lord Thomas Howard: " 'Fore God I am no
    coward;
But I cannot meet them here, for my ships are out of gear,
And the half my men are sick. I must fly, but follow quick.
We are six ships of the line; can we fight with fifty-three?"

Then spake Sir Richard Grenville: "I know you are no
    coward;
You fly them for a moment to fight with them again.
But I've ninety men and more that are lying sick ashore.   10
I should count myself the coward if I left them, my Lord
    Howard,
To these Inquisition dogs and the devildoms of Spain."

So Lord Howard passed away with five ships of war that day,
Till he melted like a cloud in the silent summer heaven;
But Sir Richard bore in hand all his sick men from the land
Very carefully and slow,
Men of Bideford in Devon,
And we laid them on the ballast down below;
For we brought them all aboard,
And they blest him in their pain, that they were not left to
    Spain,   20
To the thumbscrew and the stake, for the glory of the Lord.

He had only a hundred seamen to work the ship and to fight,
And he sailed away from Flores till the Spaniard came in
    sight,

With his huge sea-castles heaving upon the weather bow.
"Shall we fight or shall we fly?
Good Sir Richard, tell us now,
For to fight is but to die!
There'll be little of us left by the time this sun be set."
And Sir Richard said again: "We be all good English men.
Let us bang these dogs of Seville, the children of the
    devil,   30
For I never turned my back upon Don or devil yet."

Sir Richard spoke, and he laughed, and we roared a hurrah,
    and so
The little *Revenge* ran on sheer into the heart of the foe,
With her hundred fighters on deck, and her ninety sick below;
For half their fleet to the right and half to the left were seen,
And the little *Revenge* ran on through the long sea-lane
    between.

Thousands of their soldiers looked down from their decks
    and laughed,
Thousands of their seamen made mock at the mad little craft
Running on and on, till delayed
By their mountain-like *San Philip* that, of fifteen hundred
    tons,   40
And up-shadowing high above us with her yawning tiers
    of guns,
Took the breath from our sails, and we stayed.

And while now the great *San Philip* hung above us like a
    cloud
Whence the thunderbolt will fall
Long and loud,
Four galleons drew away
From the Spanish fleet that day,
And two upon the larboard and two upon the starboard lay,
And the battle-thunder broke from them all.

But anon the great *San Philip*, she bethought herself and
    went,   50
Having that within her womb that had left her ill content;
And the rest they came aboard us, and they fought us hand
    to hand,
For a dozen times they came with their pikes and
    musqueteers,
And a dozen times we shook 'em off as a dog that shakes
    his ears
When he leaps from the water to the land.

And the sun went down, and the stars came out far over
    the summer sea,
But never a moment ceased the fight of the one and the
    fifty-three.
Ship after ship the whole night long, their high-built
    galleons came,
Ship after ship, the whole night long, with her battle-thunder
    and flame;
Ship after ship, the whole night long, drew back with her
    dead and her shame.   60
For some were sunk and many were shattered, and so could
    fight us no more—
God of battles, was ever a battle like this in the world
    before?

For he said, "Fight on! fight on!"
Though his vessel was all but a wreck;
And it chanced that,, when half of the short summer night
    was gone,
With a grisly wound to be drest he had left the deck,
But a bullet struck him that was dressing it suddenly dead,
And himself he was wounded again in the side and the head,
And he said, "Fight on! fight on!"

And the night went down and the sun smiled out far over
    the summer sea,   **70**
And the Spanish fleet with broken sides lay round us all in
    a ring;
But they dared not touch us again, for they feared that we
    still could sting,
So they watched what the end would be.
And we had not fought them in vain,
But in perilous plight were we,
Seeing forty of our poor hundred were slain,
And half of the rest of us maimed for life
In the crash of the cannonades and the desperate strife;
And the sick men down in the hold were most of them stark
    and cold,
And the pikes were all broken or bent, and the powder was
    all of it spent;   **80**
And the masts and the rigging were lying over the side;

But Sir Richard cried in his English pride:
"We have fought such a fight for a day and a night
As may never be fought again!
We have won great glory, my men!
And a day less or more
At sea or ashore,
We die—does it matter when?
Sink me the ship, Master Gunner—sink her, split her in
    twain!
Fall into the hands of God, not into the hands of Spain!" **90**

And the gunner said, "Ay, ay," but the seamen made reply:
"We have children, we have wives,
And the Lord hath spared our lives.
We will make the Spaniard promise, if we yield, to let us go;
We shall live to fight again and to strike another blow."
And the lion there lay dying, and they yielded to the foe.

And the stately Spanish men to their flagship bore him then,
Where they laid him by the mast, old Sir Richard caught
at last,
And they praised him to his face with their courtly foreign
grace;
But he rose upon their decks, and he cried: 100
"I have fought for Queen and Faith like a valiant man and
true;
I have only done my duty as a man is bound to do;
With a joyful spirit I Sir Richard Grenville die!"
And he fell upon their decks, and he died.

And they stared at the dead that had been so valiant and
true,
And had holden the power and glory of Spain so cheap
That he dared her with one little ship and his English few;
Was he devil or man? He was devil for aught they knew,
But they sank his body with honour down into the deep,
And they manned the *Revenge* with a swarthier alien
crew, 110
And away she sailed with her loss and longed for her own;
When a wind from the lands they had ruined awoke from
sleep,
And the water began to heave and the weather to moan,
And or ever that evening ended a great gale blew,
And a wave like the wave that is raised by an earthquake
grew,
Till it smote upon their hulls and their sails and their masts
and their flags,
And the whole sea plunged and fell on the shot-shattered
navy of Spain,
And the little *Revenge* herself went down by the island crags
To be lost evermore in the main.

LORD TENNYSON

FLANNAN ISLE

"Though three men dwell on Flannan Isle
To keep the lamp alight,
As we steered under the lee, we caught
No glimmer through the night!"

A passing ship at dawn had brought
The news; and quickly we set sail,
To find out what strange thing might ail
The keepers of the deep-sea light.

The winter day broke blue and bright,
With glancing sun and glancing spray,   10
As o'er the swell our boat made way,
As gallant as a gull in flight.

But, as we neared the lonely Isle,
And looked up at the naked height,
And saw the lighthouse towering white,
With blinded lantern that all night
Had never shot a spark
Of comfort through the dark,
So ghostly in the cold sunlight
It seemed, that we were struck the while   20
With wonder all too dread for words.
And, as into the tiny creek
We stole beneath the hanging crag,
We saw three queer, black, ugly birds—
Too big, by far, in my belief,
For guillemot or shag—
Like seamen sitting bolt upright
Upon a half-tide reef:

But, as we neared, they plunged from sight,
Without a sound, or spurt of white.   30
And still too mazed to speak,
We landed, and made fast the boat;
And climbed the track in single file,
Each wishing he was safe afloat,
On any sea, however far,
So it be far from Flannan Isle:
And still we seemed to climb, and climb,
As though we'd lost all count of time,
And so must climb for evermore.
Yet, all too soon, we reached the door—   40
The black, sun-blistered lighthouse door,
That gaped for us ajar.

As, on the threshold, for a spell,
We paused, we seemed to breathe the smell
Of limewash and of tar,
Familiar as our daily breath,
As though 'twere some strange scent of death:
And so, yet wondering, side by side,
We stood a moment, still tongue-tied:
And each with black foreboding eyed   50
The door, ere we should fling it wide,
To leave the sunlight for the gloom:
Till, plucking courage up, at last,
Hard on each other's heels we passed
Into the living-room.

Yet, as we crowded through the door,
We only saw a table, spread
For dinner, meat, and cheese, and bread;
But all untouched; and no one there:
As though, when they sat down to eat,   60
Ere they could even taste,

73

Alarm had come; and they in haste
Had risen and left the bread and meat,
For at the table-head a chair
Lay tumbled on the floor.

We listened; but we only heard
The feeble cheeping of a bird
That starved upon its perch:
And, listening still, without a word,
We set about our hopeless search.   70
We hunted high, we hunted low,
We soon ransacked the empty house;
Then o'er the Island, to and fro,
We ranged, to listen and to look
In every cranny, cleft, or nook
That might have hid a bird or mouse:
But, though we searched from shore to shore,
We found no sign in any place:
And soon again stood face to face
Before the gaping door: 80
And stole into the room once more
As frightened children steal.
Aye: though we hunted high and low,
And hunted everywhere,
Of the three men's fate we found no trace
Of any kind in any place,
But a door ajar, and an untouched meal,
And an over-toppled chair.

And, as we listened in the gloom
Of that forsaken living-room—   90
A chill clutch on our breath—
We thought how ill-chance came to all
Who kept the Flannan Light:
And how the rock had been the death

74

Of many a likely lad:
How six had come to a sudden end,
And three had gone stark mad:
And one whom we'd all known as friend
Had leapt from the lantern one still night,
And fallen dead by the lighthouse wall: 100
And long we thought
On the three we sought,
And of what might yet befall.

Like curs a glance has brought to heel,
We listened, flinching there:
And looked, and looked, on the untouched meal
And the over-toppled chair.

We seemed to stand for an endless while,
Though still no word was said,
Three men alive on Flannan Isle,   110
Who thought on three men dead.

WILFRID GIBSON

THE TRAPPER AND THE BEARS

Outside the window howled the storm,
And made the room seem yet more warm.
Then said the drummer: "Days like these
Would make the bears and bison freeze.
Sometimes I think it would be best
To let the Red Man keep the West."
The merchant boomed expostulation:
"This weather is not cold," he said.
"Such climate makes a hardy nation.
Rough weather breeds the thoroughbred.   10

75

But I have known such cold as makes
This winter, in comparison,
Seem like a summer at the lakes,
A picnic day for everyone."
Expectant silence greeted this.
"Listen," he cried. "My tale is true."
And so he told with emphasis
A trapping story of his youth:

"The coldest day I ever knew
Was New Year's, back in '22,   20
Out in the bush near Kapuskasing,
Where, as a trapper, I was facing
The grimmest prospect I had known
Since first I started on my own.
I had no money, to begin with,
And just the clothes upon my back,
Guns, traps, an axe, a knife to skin with,
Four snarling huskies, and a shack.
The spot I'd chosen was the worst
From Porquis Junction west to Hearst—   30
At least it seemed that way to me
As rations gave out steadily
And in my traps I failed to find
Much paying fur of any kind.
To make things worse, it was my dream
To get some cash, to cease to roam,
To form a matrimonial team,
And have some kids and rear a home,
Back in some thriving little town;
For I was keen to settle down.   40

"Christmas brought neither cheer nor smiles—
The dogs and I were facing hunger
Until I trekked in, thirty miles,
To beg some food. When one is younger,

76

So piteous a case no doubt
Can blot the sun completely out,
And so, for four days I debated
This course of action that I hated.

"Next morning, I was just departing
When heavy weather checked my starting.   50
The day began with flakes of snow
That fell in droves by half past seven,
Flooding a silent world below
Out of a dark and windless heaven.
Towards evening, snowfall slackened off,
But a wild gale then smote the cabin
With shriek and sob and wail and cough
And through each cranny seemed to stab in
With icy daggers of derision,
While through the window-pane my vision   60
Saw in a maddened maelstrom go
A streaming flux of blinding snow.

"For six and thirty hours the wind
Raged madly on, and kept me pinned
There in my cabin, where my cupboard,
Like that of well-known Mrs. Hubbard,
Was grimly scant of food to feed
Me and my huskies in our need.
So, when the third day dawned at last
And all the storm was plainly past,   70
I went outside to find my sled
And mush to town to get some bread.
Giving each husky as a treat
A cast-off moccasin to eat,
I chewed in haste my last cold bannock,
And, with a certain sense of panic,
I started in a hurry, tracing
The shortest trail to Kapuskasing.

77

"A frozen creek off Woman River
Was windswept clear of all its snow.   80
My lead-dog here stopped, all a-quiver,
And when I tried to make him go,
He scratched the ice and gave a bark
That sounded like a curt remark.
I came to look. The little creek
Had frozen solid in its bed,
And in the ice, not far to seek,
Were six fresh pickerel, frozen dead.
Thus I had chopped, five minutes later,
From this first-class refrigerator,   90
A savoury dinner for my dogs
And for myself. I split some logs,
Built up a fire and fried a fish
Finer than any king could wish.
But the delay and bitter frost
Persuaded me to stop and camp,
Counting the time as safely lost
In such a long, exhausting tramp.
And so, with sleep my chief desire,
I lay down near the blazing fire.   100

"When I awoke, my dogs had vanished,
Leaving no trace that I could see
Beyond the heaving drifts that banished
All thought of stalking them for me.
The fire was out, and nature dealt
Such cold as I have never felt.
Yet in a crisis so terrific
My first desire was scientific,
An urgent impulse to be sure
About the present temperature.   110
I should have told you, in digression,
How, as a highly prized possession,
I took with me where'er I went

78

A very handy instrument—
A Fahrenheit thermometer,
To which I daily would refer.
Nor would I leave it at my shack,
For fear, before I happened back,
Some thirsty wandering Cree would call
And drain it of its alcohol.   120
So, now, I quickly got it out,
And looked, and looked—and tried to doubt
My eyes' own evidence, but no!—
It stood at ninety-eight below.

"I tried to start a fire, but found
My hands too numb to light a match;
And not an ember on the ground
Remained, on kindling wood to catch.
I shouted for my dogs. Amazed,
I heard no sound of my own voice.   130
My shouts were mute; and standing dazed,
I felt my one remaining choice
Was to keep moving down the trail
To town before my strength should fail.

"I had not gone five hundred feet
Before the cold began to get me.
I could not push on nor retreat:
My faltering snowshoes would not let me.
But just when hope was almost gone
I saw a wisp of breath-steam flow   140
Out of a fissure in the snow
Where a deep drift had formed upon
A cliff-base that in summer gave
Low access to a shallow cave.
Slipping my snowshoes off, I used them
As frantic implements to dig;
And with a vigour that abused them,

79

I reached the cave. It was not big,
But body-warmth was waiting there
To save me in my chill despair,   150
For two fat black bears in a heap
Were gently snoring in their sleep.
They were too drowsy to awake,
For when I snuggled down between them
One merely gave his paws a shake
And one growled slightly. I had seen them
Late in the autumn, by the river,
And never dreamed they would deliver
My body from a frosty fate,
But now, in a most friendly state,   160
I lay between them on my back
And dreamed about my dogs and shack.

"How long I dozed, I cannot tell,
But presently I knew right well
That further warmth my veins caressed,
And found, accounting for the heat,
Some fourteen rabbits on my chest
And two fat beavers at my feet,
While every corner round about
That my dim vision could determine   170
Was packed with squirrels, plump and stout,
And fox, and lynx, and Arctic ermine.
The most unprecedented weather
Had brought these creatures all together,
A timid, cowering set of friskers,
With frozen toes and frosty whiskers.
Of hate or rage they showed no spark,
But proved as mild in disposition
As if the beasts of Noah's Ark
Had tried an Arctic expedition,   180
And I, a sort of Gulliver,
Had crashed the berths reserved for fur.

80

In circumstances such as these,
I was, however, rightly grateful
To beasts that would not let me freeze
And meet a death forlorn and hateful.
The only lingering fear of mine
In that uncanny, beast-filled place
Was lest some thoughtless porcupine
Should make a mattress of my face.   190

"The hours passed by. I must have slept,
Although the air grew still more frigid,
And one by one the beasts that crept
About my frame were growing rigid,
Until at last the bears and I
Alone were left that did not die
Under that furry coverlet
That warded off the winter's threat.

"Next day it thawed. I ventured out,
And was surprised to hear a shout   200
Raised in my own stentorian roar
Where I had called my dogs before.
The cold had chilled my voice, you see,
And left the air-waves all congealed,
And with the rising mercury
My yells thawed out, and as they pealed
Across the snow, before my eyes
I saw my huskies all arise
Out of deep burrows they had dug
To use the snowdrifts as a rug.   210
I had a busy time that day,
Carting the fur-beasts all away
From that old cave where they had died
While I was on the under side.
I left my friends, the bears, in slumber;
But from the small beasts without number

I got such pelts that, freed from fret,
I cleared two thousand dollars net,
And gave up trapping altogether
Because I didn't like the weather.   220

"All these things happened long ago.
Since then I've wandered to and fro,
And finally have settled down
Here in this quiet little town.
I've married, too, and have acquired
Such children as I long desired:
Five boys and girls, all under ten,
Make me the happiest of men,
With pity for the senseless drone
Who has no offspring of his own.   230
Yet sometimes, when in January
Cold winds by night sweep off the prairie,
And five small kids, in search of heat,
Come to my bed to warm their feet
On me, their father, I recall
That far-off, coldest day of all.
Then at those little girls and boys
I make a sleepy, bear-like noise,
And urge them (growling hoarse and strange)
To try their mother for a change."   240

WATSON KIRKCONNELL

PAUL REVERE'S RIDE

Listen, my children, and you shall hear
Of the midnight ride of Paul Revere,
On the eighteenth of April, in Seventy-five;
Hardly a man is now alive
Who remembers that famous day and year.

He said to his friend, "If the British march
By land or sea from the town tonight,
Hang a lantern aloft in the belfry arch
Of the North Church tower as a signal light—
One, if by land, and two, if by sea;   10
And I on the opposite shore will be,
Ready to ride and spread the alarm
Through every Middlesex village and farm,
For the country-folk to be up and to arm."

Then he said, "Good-night!" and with muffled oar
Silently rowed to the Charlestown shore,
Just as the moon rose over the bay,
Where swinging wide at her moorings lay
The *Somerset*, British man-of-war;
A phantom ship, with each mast and spar   20
Across the moon like a prison bar,
And a huge black hulk, that was magnified
By its own reflection in the tide.

Meanwhile, his friend, through alley and street,
Wanders and watches with eager ears,
Till in the silence around him he hears
The muster of men at the barrack door,
The sound of arms, and the tramp of feet,
And the measured tread of the grenadiers,
Marching down to their boats on the shore.   30

Then he climbed the tower of the Old North Church,
By the wooden stairs, with stealthy tread,
To the belfry-chamber overhead,
And startled the pigeons from their perch
On the sombre rafters, that round him made
Masses and moving shapes of shade—
By the trembling ladder, steep and tall,
To the highest window in the wall,

Where he paused to listen and look down
A moment on the roofs of the town,   **40**
And the moonlight flowing over all.

Beneath, in the churchyard, lay the dead,
In their night-encampment on the hill,
Wrapped in silence so deep and still
That he could hear, like a sentinel's tread,
The watchful night-wind, as it went
Creeping along from tent to tent,
And seeming to whisper, "All is well!"
A moment only he feels the spell
Of the place and the hour, and the secret dread   **50**
Of the lonely belfry and the dead;
For suddenly all his thoughts are bent
On a shadowy something far away,
Where the river widens to meet the bay—
A line of black that bends and floats
On the rising tide, like a bridge of boats.

Meanwhile, impatient to mount and ride,
Booted and spurred, with a heavy stride
On the opposite shore walked Paul Revere.
Now he patted his horse's side,   **60**
Now gazed at the landscape far and near,
Then, impetuous, stamped the earth,
And turned and tightened his saddle-girth;
But mostly he watched with eager search
The belfry tower of the Old North Church,
As it rose above the graves on the hill,
Lonely and spectral and sombre and still.
And lo! as he looks, on the belfry's height
A glimmer, and then a gleam of light!
He springs to the saddle, the bridle he turns,   **70**
But lingers and gazes, till full on his sight
A second lamp in the belfry burns!

A hurry of hoofs in a village street,
A shape in the moonlight, a bulk in the dark,
And beneath, from the pebbles, in passing, a spark
Struck out by a steed flying fearless and fleet;
That was all! And yet, through the gloom and the light,
The fate of a nation was riding that night;
And the spark struck out by that steed in his flight,
Kindled the land into flame with its heat.   80

He has left the village and mounted the steep,
And beneath him, tranquil and broad and deep,
Is the Mystic, meeting the ocean tides;
And under the alders that skirt its edge,
Now soft on the sand, now loud on the ledge,
Is heard the tramp of his steed as he rides.

It was twelve by the village clock
When he crossed the bridge into Medford town.
He heard the crowing of the cock,
And the barking of the farmer's dog,   90
And felt the damp of the river fog,
That rises after the sun goes down.

It was one by the village clock
When he galloped into Lexington.
He saw the gilded weathercock
Swim in the moonlight as he passed,
And the meeting-house windows, blank and bare,
Gaze at him with a spectral glare,
As if they already stood aghast
At the bloody work they would look upon.   100

It was two by the village clock
When he came to the bridge in Concord town.
He heard the bleating of the flock,
And the twitter of birds among the trees,

And felt the breath of the morning breeze
Blowing over the meadows brown.
And one was safe and asleep in his bed
Who at the bridge would be first to fall,
Who that day would be lying dead,
Pierced by a British musket-ball. 110

You know the rest. In the books you have read
How the British Regulars fired and fled—
How the farmers gave them ball for ball,
From behind each fence and farmyard wall,
Chasing the redcoats down the lane,
Then crossing the fields to emerge again
Under the trees at the turn of the road,
And only pausing to fire and load.

So through the night rode Paul Revere;
And so through the night went his cry of alarm 120
To every Middlesex village and farm—
A cry of defiance and not of fear,
A voice in the darkness, a knock at the door,
And a word that shall echo for evermore!
For, borne on the night-wind of the Past,
Through all our history, to the last,
In the hour of darkness and peril and need,
The people will waken and listen to hear
The hurrying hoofbeats of that steed,
And the midnight message of Paul Revere. 130

HENRY WADSWORTH LONGFELLOW

THE DEATH OF THE HIRED MAN

Mary sat musing on the lamp-flame at the table
Waiting for Warren. When she heard his step,
She ran on tip-toe down the darkened passage
To meet him in the doorway with the news
And put him on his guard. "Silas is back."
She pushed him outward with her through the door
And shut it after her. "Be kind," she said.
She took the market things from Warren's arms
And set them on the porch, then drew him down
To sit beside her on the wooden steps.   10

"When was I ever anything but kind to him?
But I'll not have the fellow back," he said.
"I told him so last haying, didn't I?
'If he left then,' I said, 'that ended it.'
What good is he? Who else will harbour him
At his age for the little he can do?
What help he is there's no depending on.
Off he goes always when I need him most.
'He thinks he ought to earn a little pay,
Enough at least to buy tobacco with,   20
So he won't have to beg and be beholden.'
'All right,' I say, 'I can't afford to pay
Any fixed wages, though I wish I could.'
'Someone else can.' 'Then someone else will have to.'
I shouldn't mind his bettering himself
If that was what it was. You can be certain,
When he begins like that, there's someone at him
Trying to coax him off with pocket-money—
In haying time, when any help is scarce.
In winter he comes back to us. I'm done."   30

"Sh! not so loud: he'll hear you," Mary said.

"I want him to: he'll have to soon or late."

"He's worn out. He's asleep beside the stove.
When I came up from Rowe's I found him here,
Huddled against the barn-door fast asleep,
A miserable sight, and frightening, too—
You needn't smile—I didn't recognize him—
I wasn't looking for him—and he's changed.
Wait till you see."

    "Where did you say he'd been?"

"He didn't say. I dragged him to the house,   **40**
And gave him tea and tried to make him smoke.
I tried to make him talk about his travels.
Nothing would do: he just kept nodding off."

"What did he say? Did he say anything?"

"But little."

    "Anything? Mary, confess
He said he'd come to ditch the meadow for me."

"Warren!"

    "But did he? I just want to know."

"Of course he did. What would you have him say?
Surely you wouldn't grudge the poor old man
Some humble way to save his self-respect.   **50**
He added, if you really care to know,
He meant to clear the upper pasture, too.
That sounds like something you have heard before?

Warren, I wish you could have heard the way
He jumbled everything. I stopped to look
Two or three times—he made me feel so queer—
To see if he was talking in his sleep.
He ran on Harold Wilson—you remember—
The boy you had in haying four years since.
He's finished school, and teaching in his college.   60
Silas declares you'll have to get him back.
He says they two will make a team for work:
Between them they will lay this farm as smooth!
The way he mixed that in with other things.
He thinks young Wilson a likely lad, though daft
On education—you know how they fought
All through July under the blazing sun,
Silas up on the cart to build the load,
Harold along beside to pitch it on."

"Yes, I took care to keep well out of earshot."   70

"Well, those days trouble Silas like a dream.
You wouldn't think they would. How some things
    linger!
Harold's young college boy's assurance piqued him.
After so many years he still keeps finding
Good arguments he sees he might have used.
I sympathize. I know just how it feels
To think of the right thing to say too late.
Harold's associated in his mind with Latin.
He asked me what I thought of Harold's saying
He studied Latin like the violin   80
Because he liked it—that an argument!
He said he couldn't make the boy believe
He could find water with a hazel prong—
Which showed how much good school had ever done
    him.
He wanted to go over that. But most of all

89

He thinks if he could have another chance
To teach him how to build a load of hay—"

"I know, that's Silas' one accomplishment.
He bundles every forkful in its place,
And tags and numbers it for future reference,   **90**
So he can find and easily dislodge it
In the unloading. Silas does that well.
He takes it out in bunches like big birds' nests.
You never see him standing on the hay
He's trying to lift, straining to lift himself."

"He thinks if he could teach him that, he'd be
Some good perhaps to someone in the world.
He hates to see a boy the fool of books.
Poor Silas, so concerned for other folk,
And nothing to look backward to with pride,   **100**
And nothing to look forward to with hope,
So now and never any different."

Part of a moon was falling down the west,
Dragging the whole sky with it to the hills.
Its light poured softly in her lap. She saw it
And spread her apron to it. She put out her hand
Among the harp-like morning-glory strings,
Taut with the dew from garden bed to eaves,
As if she played unheard some tenderness
That wrought on him beside her in the night.   **110**
"Warren," she said, "he has come home to die:
You needn't be afraid he'll leave you this time."

"Home," he mocked gently.

          "Yes, what else but home?
It all depends on what you mean by home.
Of course he's nothing to us, any more

Than was the hound that came a stranger to us
Out of the woods, worn out upon the trail."

"Home is the place where, when you have to go there
They have to take you in."

                    "I should have called it
Something you somehow haven't to deserve."   120

Warren leaned out and took a step or two,
Picked up a little stick, and brought it back
And broke it in his hand and tossed it by.
"Silas has better claim on us you think
Than on his brother? Thirteen little miles
As the road winds would bring him to his door.
Silas has walked that far no doubt today.
Why didn't he go there? His brother's rich,
A somebody—director in the bank."

"He never told us that."

                    "We know it though."   130

"I think his brother ought to help, of course.
I'll see to that if there is need. He ought of right
To take him in, and might be willing to—
He may be better than appearances.
But have some pity on Silas. Do you think
If he had any pride in claiming kin
Or anything he looked for from his brother,
He'd keep so still about him all this time?"

"I wonder what's between them."

                    "I can tell you.
Silas is what he is—we wouldn't mind him—   140
But just the kind that kinsfolk can't abide.

91

He never did a thing so very bad.
He don't know why he isn't quite as good
As anybody. Worthless though he is,
He won't be made ashamed to please his brother."

"I can't think Si ever hurt anyone."

"No, but he hurt my heart the way he lay
And rolled his old head on that sharp-edged chair-back.
He wouldn't let me put him on the lounge.
You must go in and see what you can do.   150
I made the bed up for him there tonight.
You'll be surprised at him—how much he's broken.
His working days are done; I'm sure of it."

"I'd not be in a hurry to say that."

"I haven't been. Go, look, see for yourself.
But, Warren, please remember how it is:
He's come to help you ditch the meadow.
He has a plan. You mustn't laugh at him.
He may not speak of it, and then he may.
I'll sit and see if that small sailing cloud   160
Will hit or miss the moon."

          It hit the moon.
Then there were three there, making a dim row,
The moon, the little silver cloud, and she.

Warren returned—too soon, it seemed to her,
Slipped to her side, caught up her hand and waited.

"Warren?" she questioned.

          "Dead," was all he answered.

                              ROBERT FROST

SAM'S THREE WISHES

"I'm thinking and thinking," said old Sam Shore,
" 'Twere somebody *knocking* I heard at the door."
From the clock popped the cuckoo and cuckooed out eight,
As there in his chair he wondering sate . . .
"There's no one I knows on would come so late,
A-clicking the latch of an empty house
With nobbut inside 'un but me and a mouse . . .
Maybe a-waking in sleep I be,
And 'twere out of a dream came that tapping to me."
At length he cautiously rose and went,   **10**
And with thumb upon latch awhile listening bent,
Then slowly drew open the door. And behold!
There stood a Fairy!—all green and gold,
Mantled up warm against dark and cold,
And smiling up into his candle shine,
Lips like wax, and cheeks like wine,
As saucy and winsome a thing to see
As are linden buds on a linden tree.

Stock-still in the doorway stood simple Sam
A-ducking his head, with "Good-e'en to 'ee, Ma'am."   **20**
Dame Fairy she nods, and cries clear and sweet,
" 'Tis a *very* good-e'en, sir, when such folks meet.
I know thee, Sam, though thou wist not of me,
And I'm come in late gloaming to speak with thee;
Though my eyes do dazzle at glint of your rush,
All under this pretty green fuchsia bush."

Sam ducked once more, smiling simple and slow.
Like the warbling of birds her words did flow,
And she laughed, very merry, to see how true

93

Shone the old man's kindness his courtesy through.   30
And she nodded her head, and the stars on high
Sparkled down on her smallness from out of the sky.

"A friend is a friend, Sam, and wonderful pleasant,
And I'm come for old sake's sake to bring thee a present.
Three wishes, three wishes are thine, Sam Shore.
Just three wishes—and wish no more.
All for because, ruby-ripe to see,
The pixy-pears burn in yon hawthorn tree,
And your old milch cow, wheresoever she goes,
Never crops over the fairy-knowes.   40
Ay, Sam, thou art old and thy house is lone,
But there's Potencies round thee, and here is one!"

Poor Sam, he stared: and the stars o'erhead
A shimmering light on the elm-tops shed.
Like rilling of water her voice rang sweet,
And the night-wind sighed at the sound of it.

He frowned—glanced back at the empty grate,
And shook very slowly his grey old pate:
"Three wishes, my dear! Why, I scarcely knows
Which be my crany and which my toes!   50
But I thank 'ee, Ma'am, kindly, and this I'd say,
That the night of your passing is Michaelmas Day;
And if it were company come on a sudden,
Why, I'd ax for a fat goose to fry in the oven!"

And lo, and forsooth! as the words he was uttering,
A rich puff of air set his candle a-guttering,
And there rose in the kitchen a sizzling and sputtering,
With a crackling of sparks and of flames a great fluttering,
And—of which there could not be two opinions—
A smoking-hot savour of sage and onions.   60

94

Beam, wall and flagstones, the kitchen was lit,
Every dark corner and cranny of it,
With the blaze from the hearthstone. Copper and brass
Winked back the winking of platter and glass.
And a wonderful squeaking of mice went up
At the smell of a Michaelmas supper to sup—
Unctuous odours that wreathed and swirled
Where'er frisked a whisker or mouse-tail twirled,
While out of the chimney up into the night
That ne'er-to-be-snuffed-too-much smoke took flight. **70**
"That's one," says the Fairy, finger on thumb,
"So now, Mister Sam, there's but two to come!"
She leaned her head sidelong; she lifted her chin,
With a twinkling of eye from the radiance within.
Poor Sam stood stounded; he says, says he,
"I *wish* my old Mother was back with me,
For if there was one thing she couldn't refuse,
'Twas a sweet thick slice from the breast of a goose."
But his cheek grew stiff and his eyes stared bright
For there, on her stick, pushing out of the night, **80**
Tap-tapping along, herself and no other,
Came who but the shape of his dear old Mother!
Straight into the kitchen she hastened and went,
Her breath coming quick as if all but spent,
"Why Sam," says she, "the bird be turning,
For my nose tells I that the skin's a-burning!"
And down at the oven the ghost of her sat
And basted the goose with the boiling fat.

"Oho," cries the Fairy, sweet and small,
"Another wish gone will leave nothing at all!" **90**
And Sam sighs, "Bless 'ee, Ma'am, keep the other,
There's nowt that I want now I have my Mother."

But the Fairy laughs softly, and says, says she,
"There's one wish left, Sam; I promised 'ee three.

95

Hasten your wits, the hour creeps on,
There's calling afield and I'm soon to be gone.
Soon as haps midnight the cocks will crow,
And me to the gathering and feasting must go."

Sam gazed at his Mother—withered and wan,
The rose in her cheek, her bright hair, gone,   100
And her poor old back bent double with years—
And he scarce could speak for the salt, salt tears.
"Well, well," he says, "I'm unspeakable glad:
But—it bain't quite the same as when I was a lad.
There's joy and there's joy, Ma'am, but to tell 'ee the **truth**
There's none can compare with the joy of one's youth.
And if it was possible, how could I choose
But be back in boy's breeches to eat the goose;
And all the old things, and my Mother the most,
To shine again real as my own gatepost!   110
What wouldn't I give, too, to see again wag
The dumpity tail of my old dog, Shag!
Your kindness, Ma'am, but all wishing was **vain**
Unless us can both be young again."
A shrill faint laughter from nowhere came. . . .
Empty the dark in the candle-flame. . . .
And there stood our Sam, about four foot high,
Snub nose, shock hair, and round blue eye.
Breeches and braces and coat of him too,
Shirt on his back, and each clodhopping shoe   120
Had shrunk to a nicety—button and hem
To fit the small Sammie tucked up into them.

There was his Mother, too, smooth, clear cheek,
Lips as sooth as a blackbird's beak;
Pretty arched eyebrows, the daintiest nose—
While the smoke of the baking deliciously rose.

96

"Come, Sammie," she cries, "your old Mammikin's joy,
Climb up on your stool, supper's ready, my boy.
Bring in the candle, and shut out the night;
There's goose, baked 'taties and cabbage to bite.   130
Why, bless the wee lamb, he's all shiver and shake,
And you'd think from the look of him scarcely awake!
If 'ee glour wi' those eyes, Sam, so dark and round,
The elves will away with 'ee, I'll be bound!"
So Sam and his Mother by wishes three
Were made just as happy as happy can be.
And there—with a bumpity tail to wag—
Sat laughing with tongue out, their old dog, Shag.
To clatter of platter, bones, giblets and juice,
Between them they ate up the whole of the goose.   140

But time is a river for ever in flow,
The weeks went by as the weeks must go;
Soon fifty-two to a year did grow.
The long years passed, one after another,
Making older and older our Sam and his Mother;
And, alas and alack, with nine of them gone,
Poor Shag lay asleep again under a stone.
And a sorrowful dread would sometimes creep
Into Sam's dreams, as he lay asleep,
That his Mother was lost, and away he'd fare,   150
Calling her, calling her, everywhere,
In dark, in rain, by roads unknown,
Under echoing hills, and alone, alone.
What bliss in the morning to wake and see
The sun shining green in the linden tree,
And out of that dream's dark shadowiness
To slip in on his Mother and give her a kiss,
Then go whistling off in the dew to hear
The thrushes all mocking him, sweet and clear.

97

Still, moon after moon from heaven above   **160**
Shone on Mother and son, and made light of love.
Her roses faded, her pretty brown hair
Had sorrowful grey in it everywhere.
And at last she died, and was laid to rest,
Her tired hands crossed on her shrunken breast.
And Sam, now lonely, lived on and on
Till most of his workaday life seemed gone.

Yet spring came again, with its green and blue,
And presently summer's wild roses too,
Pinks, Sweet-William, and sops-in-wine,   **170**
Blackberry, lavender, eglantine.
And when these had blossomed and gone their way,
'Twas apples and daisies and Michaelmas Day—
Yes, spider-webs, dew, and haws in the may,
And seraphs singing in Michaelmas Day.

Sam worked all morning and *couldn't* get rest
For a kind of a feeling of grief in his breast.
And yet, not grief, but something more
Like the thought that what happens has happened before.
He fed the chickens, he fed the sow,   **180**
On a three-legged stool sate down to the cow,
With a pail 'twixt his legs in the green in the meadow,
Under the elm trees' lengthening shadow;
And woke at last with a smile and a sigh
To find he had milked his poor Jingo dry.

As dusk set in, even the birds did seem
To be calling and calling from out of a dream.
He chopped up kindling, shut up his shed,
In a bucket of well-water soused his head
To freshen his eyes up a little and make   **190**
The drowsy old wits of him wider awake.

As neat as a womanless creature is able
He swept up his hearthstone and laid the table.
And then o'er his platter and mug, if you please,
Sate gloomily gooming at loaf and cheese—
Gooming and gooming as if the mere sight
Of his victuals could satisfy appetite!
And the longer and longer he looked at them
The slimmer slimmed upward his candle flame,
Blue in the air. And when squeaked a mouse,   200
'Twas loud as a trump in the hush of the house.
Then, sudden, a soft little wind puffed by,
'Twixt the thick-thatched roof and the star-sown sky;
And died. And then
That deep, dead, wonderful silence again.
Then—soft as a rattle a-counting her seeds
In the midst of a tangle of withered-up weeds—
Came a faint, faint knocking, a rustle like silk,
And a breath at the keyhole as soft as milk—
Still as the flit of a moth. And then . . .   210
That infinitesimal knocking again.

Sam lifted his chin from his fists. He listened.
His wandering eyes in the candle glistened.
Then slowly, slowly, rolled round by degrees—
And there sat a mouse on the top of his cheese.
He stared at this Midget, and it at him,
Over the edge of his mug's round rim,
And—as if it were Christian—he says, "Did 'ee hear
A faint little tap-tap-tap-tapping, my dear?

"You was at supper and me in a maze;   220
'Tis dark for a caller in these lone days,
There's nowt in the larder. We're both of us old,
And all of my loved ones sleep under the mould,
And yet—and yet—as I've told 'ee before . . ."

But if Sam's story you'd read to the end,
Turn back to page one, and press onward, dear friend;
Yes, if you would stave the last note of this song,
Turn back to page primus, and warble along!
For all sober records of life (come to write 'em)
Are bound to continue—well, ad infinitum.   230

WALTER DE LA MARE

I'LL FIND A WAY OR MAKE IT

It was a noble Roman,
  In Rome's imperial day,
Who heard a coward croaker
  Before the castle say,—
"They're safe in such a fortress;
  There is no way to shake it!"
"On! on!" exclaimed the hero;
  "I'll find a way, or make it!"

Is fame your aspiration?
  Her path is steep and high;   10
In vain he seeks her temple,
  Content to gaze and sigh.
The shining throne is waiting,
  But he alone can take it
Who says, with Roman firmness,
  "I'll find a way, or make it!"

Is learning your ambition?
  There is no royal road;
Alike the peer and peasant
  Must climb to her abode;   20
Who feels the thirst for knowledge,

100

In Helicon may slake it,
If he has still the Roman will
   "To find a way, or make it!"

Are riches worth the getting?
   They must be bravely sought;
With wishing and with fretting
   The boon can not be bought;
To all the prize is open,
   But only he can take it,   30
Who says, with Roman courage,
   "I'll find a way, or make it!"

JOHN GODFREY SAXE

LONE DOG

I'm a lean dog, a keen dog, a wild dog, and lone;
I'm a rough dog, a tough dog, hunting on my own;
I'm a bad dog, a mad dog, teasing silly sheep;
I love to sit and bay the moon, to keep fat souls from sleep.

I'll never be a lap dog, licking dirty feet,
A sleek dog, a meek dog, cringing for my meat,
Not for me the fireside, the well-filled plate,
But shut door, and sharp stone, and cuff, and kick, and hate.

Not for me the other dogs, running by my side,
Some have run a short while, but none of them would
    bide.   10
O mine is still the lone trail, the hard trail, the best,
Wide wind, and wild stars, and the hunger of the quest!

IRENE RUTHERFORD McLEOD

OLD IRONSIDES

Ay, tear her tattered ensign down!
  Long has it waved on high,
And many an eye has danced to see
  That banner in the sky;
Beneath it rung the battle shout,
  And burst the cannon's roar:
The meteor of the ocean air
  Shall sweep the clouds no more!

Her deck, once red with heroes' blood,
  Where knelt the vanquished foe,   **10**
When winds were hurrying o'er the flood
  And waves were white below,
No more shall feel the victor's tread,
  Or know the conquered knee:
The harpies of the shore shall pluck
  The eagle of the sea!

Oh, better that her shattered hulk
  Should sink beneath the wave!
Her thunders shook the mighty deep,
  And there should be her grave;   **20**
Nail to the mast her holy flag,
  Set every threadbare sail,
And give her to the god of storms,
  The lightning and the gale!

OLIVER WENDELL HOLMES

LITTLE BATEESE

You bad leetle boy, not moche you care
How busy you're kipin' your poor gran'père
Tryin' to stop you ev'ry day
Chasin' de hen around de hay—
W'y don't you geev' dem a chance to lay,
                Leetle Bateese!

Off on de fiel' you foller de plough,
Den w'en you're tire you scare de cow,
Sickin' de dog till dey jomp de wall
So de milk ain't good for not'ing at all—   10
An' you're only five an' a half dis fall,
                Leetle Bateese!

Too sleepy for sayin' de prayer to-night?
Never min', I s'pose it'll be all right,
Say dem to-morrow—ah! dere he go!
Fas' asleep in a minute or so—
And he'll stay like dat till de rooster crow,
                Leetle Bateese!

Den wake us up right away toute suite,
Lookin' for somet'ing more to eat,   20
Makin' me t'ink of dem long-leg crane,
Soon as dey swaller, dey start again.
I wonder your stomach don't get no pain,
                Leetle Bateese!

But see him now lyin' dere in bed,
Look at de arm onderneath hees head;
If he grow lak dat till he's twenty year

103

I bet he'll be stronger dan Louis Cyr,
An' beat all de voyageur leevin' here,
                    Leetle Bateese!   30

Jus' feel de muscle along hees back,
Won't geev heem moche bodder for carry pack
On de long portage, any size canoe,
Dere's not many t'ing dat boy won't do,
For he's got double-joint on hees body too,
                    Leetle Bateese!

But, leetle Bateese! please don't forget
We rader you're stayin' de small boy yet;
So chase de chicken an' mak' dem scare,
An' do w'at you lak wit' your gran'père,   40
For w'en you're beeg feller he won't be dere—
                    Leetle Bateese!

WILLIAM HENRY DRUMMOND

SEA-FEVER

I must go down to the seas again, to the lonely sea and the
    sky,
And all I ask is a tall ship, and a star to steer her by;
And the wheel's kick and the wind's song and the white sail's
    shaking,
And a grey mist on the sea's face, and a grey dawn breaking.

I must go down to the seas again, for the call of the running
    tide
Is a wild call and a clear call that may not be denied;
And all I ask is a windy day with the white clouds flying,
And the flung spray and the blown spume, and the sea-gulls
    crying.

104

I must go down to the seas again, to the vagrant gypsy life,
To the gull's way and the whale's way where the wind's like a
     whetted knife;   10
And all I ask is a merry yarn from a laughing fellow rover,
And quiet sleep and a sweet dream when the long trick's
     over.

JOHN MASEFIELD

MIA CARLOTTA

Giuseppe, da barber, ees greata for "mash",
He gotta da bigga, da blacka mustache,
Good clo'es an' good styla an' playnta good cash.

W'enevra Giuseppe ees walk on da street,
Da people dey talka, "how nobby! how neat!
How softa da handa, how smalla da feet."

He raisa hees hat an' he shaka hees curls,
An' smila weeth teetha so shiny like pearls;
O! many da heart of da seelly young girls
          He gotta.   10
        Yes, playnta he gotta—
          But notta
          Carlotta!

Giuseppe, da barber, he maka da eye,
An' lika da steam engine puffa an' sigh
For catcha Carlotta w'en she ees go by.

Carlotta she walka weeth nose in da air,
An' look through Giuseppe weeth far-away stare,
As eef she no see dere ees som'body dere.

105

Giuseppe, da barber, he gotta da cash,   **20**
He gotta da clo'es an' da bigga mustache.
He gotta da seelly young girls for da "mash",
      But notta—
    You bat my life, notta—
        Carlotta.
        I gotta!

THOMAS A. DALY

A VAGABOND SONG

There is something in the autumn which is native to my
    blood—
Touch of manner, hint of mood;
And my heart is like a rhyme,
With the yellow and the purple and the crimson keeping
    time.

The scarlet of the maples can shake me like a cry
Of bugles going by.
And my lonely spirit thrills
To see the frosty asters like a smoke upon the hills.

There is something in October sets the gipsy blood astir;
We must rise and follow her,   **10**
When from every hill of flame
She calls and calls each vagabond by name.

BLISS CARMAN

CALLED UP

Come, tumble up, Lord Nelson, the British Fleet's a-looming!
Come, show a leg, Lord Nelson, the guns they are a-booming!
'Tis a longish line of battle, such as we did never see;
An' 'tis not the same old round shot as was fired by you an' me!

What see'st thou, Sir Francis?—Strange things I see appearing!
What hearest thou, Sir Francis?—Strange sounds I do be hearing!
They are fighting in the heavens; they're at war beneath the sea!
Ay, their ways are mighty different from the ways o' you an' me!

See'st thou naught else, Sir Francis?—I see great lights a-seeking!
Hearest thou naught else, Sir Francis?—I hear thin wires a-speaking!   10
Three leagues that shot hath carried!—God, that such could ever be!
There's no mortal doubt, Lord Nelson—they ha' done wi' you and me!

Look thou again, Sir Francis!—I see the flags a-flapping!
Hearken once more, Sir Francis!—I hear the sticks a-tapping!
'Tis a sight that calls me thither!—'Tis a sound that bids me "Come!"
'Tis the old Trafalgar signal!—'Tis the beating of my drum!

107

Art thou ready, good Sir Francis? See, they wait upon the
quay!—

Praise be to God, Lord Nelson, they ha' thought of you
an' me!

DUDLEY CLARK

THE MONKEY

I saw you hunched and shivering on the stones,
The bleak wind piercing to your fragile bones,
Your shabby scarlet all inadequate:
A little ape that had such human eyes
They seemed to hide behind their miseries—
Their dumb and hopeless bowing down to fate—
Some puzzled wonder. Was your monkey soul
Sickening with memories of gorgeous days,
Of tropic playfellows and forest ways,
Where, agile, you could swing from bole to bole   10
In an enchanted twilight with great flowers
For stars; or on a bough the long night hours
Sit out in rows, and chatter at the moon?
Shuffling you went, your tiny chilly hand
Outstretched for what you did not understand;
Your puckered mournful face begging a boon
That but enslaved you more. They who passed by
Saw nothing sorrowful; gave laugh or stare,
Unheeding that the little antic there
Played in the gutter such a tragedy.   20

NANCY CAMPBELL

108

IN FLANDERS FIELDS

In Flanders fields the poppies blow
Between the crosses row on row,
    That mark our place; and in the sky
    The larks, still bravely singing, fly
Scarce heard amid the guns below.

We are the Dead. Short days ago
We lived, felt dawn, saw sunset glow,
    Loved and were loved, and now we lie
        In Flanders fields.

Take up our quarrel with the foe;   10
To you from failing hands we throw
    The torch; be yours to hold it high.
    If ye break faith with us who die
We shall not sleep, though poppies grow
        In Flanders fields.

JOHN McCRAE

THE DONKEY

When fishes flew and forests walked
    And figs grew upon thorn,
Some moment when the moon was blood
    Then surely I was born;

With monstrous head and sickening cry
    And ears like errant wings,

The devil's walking parody
    Of all four-footed things.

The tattered outlaw of the earth,
    Of ancient crooked will;   10
Starve, scourge, deride me: I am dumb,
    I keep my secret still.

Fools! For I also had my hour;
    One far fierce hour and sweet:
There was a shout about my ears,
    And palms before my feet.

GILBERT KEITH CHESTERTON

LINCOLN

There was a boy of other days,
A quiet, awkward, earnest lad,
Who trudged long weary miles to get
A book on which his heart was set—
And then no candle had!

He was too poor to buy a lamp
But very wise in woodmen's ways.
He gathered seasoned bough and stem,
And crisping leaf, and kindled them
Into a ruddy blaze.   10

Then as he lay full length and read,
The firelight flickered on his face
And etched his shadow on the gloom,
And made a picture in the room,
In that most humble place.

The hard years came, the hard years went,
But, gentle, brave, and strong of will,
He met them all. And when today
We see his pictured face, we say,
"There's light upon it still."   **20**

NANCY BYRD TURNER

WANDER-THIRST

Beyond the East the sunrise, beyond the West the sea,
And East and West the wander-thirst that will not let me be;
It works in me like madness, dear, to bid me say good-bye;
For the seas call, and the stars call, and oh! the call of the
    sky!

I know not where the white road runs, nor what the blue
    hills are,
But a man can have the sun for friend, and for his guide a
    star;
And there's no end of voyaging when once a voice is heard,
For the river calls, and the road calls, and oh! the call of a
    bird!

Yonder the long horizon lies, and there by night and day
The old ships draw to home again, the young ships sail
    away;   **10**
And come I may, but go I must, and if men ask you why,
You may put the blame on the stars and the sun, and the
    white road and the sky!

GERALD GOULD

PART TWO

BANNERMAN OF THE DANDENONG

I rode through the Bush in the burning noon
    Over the hills to my bride,—
The track was rough and the way was long,
And Bannerman of the Dandenong,
    He rode along by my side.

A day's march off my Beautiful dwelt,
    By the Murray streams in the West;—
Lightly lilting a gay love-song
Rode Bannerman of the Dandenong,
    With a blood-red rose on his breast.   10

"Red, red rose of the Western streams"
    Was the song he sang that day—
Truest comrade in hour of need;
Bay Mathinna his peerless steed—
    I had my own good grey.

There fell a spark on the upland grass—
    The dry Bush leapt into flame;—
And I felt my heart go cold as death,
And Bannerman smiled and caught his breath—
    But I heard him name Her name.   20

Down the hillside the fire-floods rushed,
    On the roaring eastern wind;—
Neck and neck was the reckless race,—
Ever the bay mare kept her pace,
    But the grey horse dropped behind.

He turned in the saddle—"Let's change, I say!"
   And his bridle rein he drew.
He sprang to the ground,—"Look sharp!" he said,
With a backward toss of his curly head—
   "I ride lighter than you!"   30

Down and up—it was quickly done—
   No words to waste that day!—
Swift as a swallow she sped along,
The good bay mare from Dandenong,—
   And Bannerman rode the grey.

The hot air scorched like a furnace blast
   From the very mouth of Hell:—
The blue gums caught and blazed on high
Like flaming pillars into the sky; . . .
   The grey horse staggered and fell.   40

"Ride, ride, lad,—ride for her sake!" he cried;—
   Into the gulf of flame
Were swept, in less than a breathing space,
The laughing eyes, and the comely face,
   And the lips that named *Her* name.

She bore me bravely, the good bay mare;—
   Stunned, and dizzy and blind,
I heard the sound of a mingling roar—
'Twas the river's rush that I heard before,
   And the flames that rolled behind.   50

Safe—safe, at Nammoora gate,
   I fell, and lay like a stone.
O love! thine arms were about me then,
Thy warm tears called me to life again,—
   But—O God! that I came alone!—

I and my Beautiful dwell in peace,
  By the Murray streams in the West,—
But oft through the mist of my dreams along
Rides Bannerman of the Dandenong,
  With the blood-red rose on his breast.   60

ALICE WERNER

FIDELE'S GRASSY TOMB

The Squire sat propped in a pillowed chair,
His eyes were alive and clear of care,
But well he knew that the hour was come
To bid good-bye to his ancient home.

He looked on garden, wood, and hill,
He looked on the lake, sunny and still:
The last of earth that his eyes could see
Was the island church of Orchardleigh.

The last that his heart could understand
Was the touch of the tongue that licked his hand: 10
"Bury the dog at my feet," he said,
And his voice dropped, and the Squire was dead.

Now the dog was a hound of the Danish breed,
Staunch to love and strong at need:
He had dragged his master safe to shore
When the tide was ebbing at Elsinore.

From that day forth, as reason would,
He was named "Fidele", and made it good:
When the last of the mourners left the door
Fidele was dead on the chantry floor.   20

117

They buried him there at his master's feet,
And all that heard of it deemed it meet:
The story went the rounds for years,
Till it came at last to the Bishop's ears.

Bishop of Bath and Wells was he,
Lord of the lords of Orchardleigh;
And he wrote to the Parson the strongest screed
That Bishop may write or Parson read.

The sum of it was that a soulless hound
Was known to be buried in hallowed ground;   30
From scandal sore the Church to save
They must take the dog from his master's grave.

The heir was far in a foreign land,
The Parson was wax to my Lord's command:
He sent for the Sexton and bade him make
A lonely grave by the shore of the lake.

The Sexton sat by the water's brink
Where he used to sit when he used to think;
He reasoned slow, but he reasoned it out,
And his argument left him free from doubt.   40

"A Bishop," he said, "is the top of his trade:
But there's others can give him a start with the spade:
Yon dog, he carried the Squire ashore,
And a Christian couldn't ha' done no more."

The grave was dug, the mason came
And carved on stone Fidele's name:
But the dog that the Sexton laid inside
Was a dog that never had lived or died.

So the Parson was praised, and the scandal stayed,
Till, a long time after, the church decayed,　　**50**
And, laying the floor anew, they found
In the tomb of the Squire the bones of a hound.

As for the Bishop of Bath and Wells
No more of him the story tells;
Doubtless he lived as a Prelate and Prince,
And died and was buried a century since.

And whether his view was right or wrong
Has little to do with this my song;
Something we owe him, you must allow;
And perhaps he has changed his mind by now.　　**60**

The Squire in the family chantry sleeps,
The marble still his memory keeps:
Remember, when the name you spell,
There rest Fidele's bones as well.

For the Sexton's grave you need not search,
'Tis a nameless mound by the island church:
An ignorant fellow, of humble lot—
But he knew one thing that a Bishop did not.

SIR HENRY NEWBOLT

SIMON LEGREE
(A Negro Sermon)

Legree's big house was white and green.
His cotton-fields were the best to be seen.
He had strong horses and opulent cattle,
And bloodhounds bold, with chains that would
    rattle.
His garret was full of curious things:
Books of magic, bags of gold,
And rabbits' feet on long twine strings.
But he went down to the Devil.

Legree he sported a brass-buttoned coat,
A snake-skin necktie, a blood-red shirt.   **10**
Legree he had a beard like a goat,
And a thick hairy neck, and eyes like dirt.
His puffed-out cheeks were fish-belly white,
He had great long teeth, and an appetite.
He ate raw meat, 'most every meal,
And rolled his eyes till the cat would squeal.
His fist was an enormous size
To mash poor niggers that told him lies:
He was surely a witch-man in disguise.
But he went down to the Devil.   **20**

He wore hip-boots, and would wade all day
To capture his slaves that had fled away.
But he went down to the Devil.
He beat poor Uncle Tom to death
Who prayed for Legree with his last breath.
Then Uncle Tom to Eva flew,
To the high sanctoriums bright and new;

And Simon Legree stared up beneath,
And cracked his heels, and ground his teeth:
And went down to the Devil.   30

He crossed the yard in the storm and gloom;
He went into his grand front room.
He said, "I killed him, and I don't care."
He kicked a hound, he gave a swear;
He tightened his belt, he took a lamp,
Went down cellar to the webs and damp.
There in the middle of the mouldy floor
He heaved up a slab, he found a door—
And went down to the Devil.

His lamp blew out, his eyes burned bright.   40
Simon Legree stepped down all night—
Down, down to the Devil.
Simon Legree he reached the place,
He saw one half of the human race,
He saw the Devil on a wide green throne,
Gnawing the meat from a big ham-bone,
And he said to Mister Devil:

    "I see that you have much to eat—
    A red ham-bone is surely sweet.
    I see that you have lion's feet;   50
    I see your frame is fat and fine,
    I see you drink your poison wine—
    Blood and burning turpentine."

And the Devil said to Simon Legree:
    "I like your style, so wicked and free.
    Come sit and share my throne with me,
    And let us bark and revel."
And there they sit and gnash their teeth,

121

And each one wears a hop-vine wreath.
They are matching pennies and shooting craps,   60
And old Legree is fat and fine:
He eats the fire and drinks the wine—
Blood and burning turpentine—
  Down, down with the Devil;
    Down, down with the Devil;
      Down, down with the Devil.

VACHEL LINDSAY

HEATHER ALE

From the bonny bells of heather
  They brewed a drink long-syne,
Was sweeter far than honey,
  Was stronger far than wine.
They brewed it and they drank it,
  And lay in a blessed swound
For days and days together
  In their dwellings underground.

There rose a king in Scotland,
  A fell man to his foes,   10
He smote the Picts in battle,
  He hunted them like roes.
Over miles of the red mountain
  He hunted as they fled,
And strewed the dwarfish bodies
  Of the dying and the dead.

Summer came in the country,
  Red was the heather bell;
But the manner of the brewing

122

Was none alive to tell.   **20**
In graves that were like children's
  On many a mountain head,
The Brewsters of the Heather
  Lay numbered with the dead.

The king in the red moorland
  Rode on a summer's day;
And the bees hummed, and the curlews
  Cried beside the way.
The king rode, and was angry,
  Black was his brow and pale,   **30**
To rule in a land of heather
  And lack the Heather Ale.

It fortuned that his vassals,
  Riding free on the heath,
Came on a stone that was fallen
  And vermin hid beneath.
Rudely plucked from their hiding,
  Never a word they spoke:
A son and his agèd father—
  Last of the dwarfish folk.   **40**

The king sat high on his charger,
  He looked on the little men;
And the dwarfish and swarthy couple
  Looked at the king again.
Down by the shore he had them;
  And there on the giddy brink—
"I will give you life, ye vermin,
  For the secret of the drink."

There stood the son and father,
  And they looked high and low;   **50**
The heather was red around them,

123

The sea rumbled below.
And up and spoke the father,
Shrill was his voice to hear:
"I have a word in private,
A word for the royal ear.

"Life is dear to the agèd,
And honour a little thing;
I would gladly sell the secret,"
Quoth the Pict to the king.   60
His voice was small as a sparrow's,
And shrill and wonderful clear:
"I would gladly sell my secret,
Only my son I fear.

"For life is a little matter,
And death is naught to the young;
And I dare not sell my honour
Under the eye of my son.
Take *him*, O king, and bind him,
And cast him far in the deep;   70
And it's I will tell the secret
That I have sworn to keep."

They took the son and bound him,
Neck and heels in a thong,
And a lad took him and swung him,
And flung him far and strong,
And the sea swallowed his body,
Like that of a child of ten;—
And there on the cliff stood the father,
Last of the dwarfish men.   80

"True was the word I told you:
Only my son I feared;
For I doubt the sapling courage

124

That goes without the beard.
But now in vain is the torture,
   Fire shall never avail:
Here dies in my bosom
   The secret of Heather Ale."

ROBERT LOUIS STEVENSON

THE FORSAKEN

I

Once in the winter
Out on a lake
In the heart of the north-land,
Far from the Fort
And far from the hunters,
A Chippewa woman
With her sick baby,
Crouched in the last hours
Of a great storm.
Frozen and hungry,   10
She fished through the ice
With a line of the twisted
Bark of the cedar,
And a rabbit-bone hook
Polished and barbed;
Fished with the bare hook
All through the wild day,
Fished and caught nothing;
While the young chieftain
Tugged at her breasts,   20
Or slept in the lacings
Of the warm *tikanagan*.

All the lake-surface
Streamed with the hissing
Of millions of iceflakes
Hurled by the wind;
Behind her the round
Of a lonely island
Roared like a fire
With the voice of the storm   30
In the deeps of the cedars.
Valiant, unshaken,
She took of her own flesh,
Baited the fish-hook,
Drew in a grey-trout,
Drew in his fellows,
Heaped them beside her,
Dead in the snow.
Valiant, unshaken,
She faced the long distance,   40
Wolf-haunted and lonely,
Sure of her goal
And the life of her dear one:
Tramped for two days,
On the third in the morning,
Saw the strong bulk
Of the Fort by the river,
Saw the wood-smoke
Hang soft in the spruces,
Heard the keen yelp   50
Of the ravenous huskies
Fighting for whitefish:
Then she had rest.

II

Years and years after,
When she was old and withered,

126

When her son was an old man
And his children filled with vigour,
They came in their northern tour on the verge of
    winter,
To an island in a lonely lake.
There one night they camped, and on the morrow 60
Gathered their kettles and birch-bark,
Their rabbit-skin robes and their mink-traps,
Launched their canoes and slunk away through the
    islands,
Left her alone forever,
Without a word of farewell,
Because she was old and useless,
Like a paddle broken and warped,
Or a pole that was splintered.
Then, without a sigh,
Valiant, unshaken,   70
She smoothed her dark locks under her kerchief,
Composed her shawl in state,
Then folded her hands ridged with sinews and corded
    with veins,
Folded them across her breasts spent with the
    nourishing of children,
Gazed at the sky past the tops of the cedars,
Saw two spangled nights arise out of the twilight,
Saw two days go by filled with the tranquil sunshine,
Saw, without pain, or dread, or even a moment of
    longing:
Then on the third great night there came thronging
    and thronging
Millions of snowflakes out of a windless cloud;   80
They covered her close with a beautiful crystal
    shroud,
Covered her deep and silent.
But in the frost of the dawn,

Up from the life below,
Rose a column of breath
Through a tiny cleft in the snow,
Fragile, delicately drawn,
Wavering with its own weakness,
In the wilderness a sign of the spirit,
Persisting still in the sight of the sun   90
Till day was done.
Then all light was gathered up by the hand of God
          and hid in His breast,
Then there was born a silence deeper than silence,
Then she had rest.

DUNCAN CAMPBELL SCOTT

ETIQUETTE

The *Ballyshannon* foundered off the coast of Cariboo,
And down in fathoms many went the captain and the crew;
Down went the owners—greedy men whom hope of gain
          allured:
Oh, dry the starting tear, for they were heavily insured.

Besides the captain and the mate, the owners and the crew,
The passengers were also drowned excepting only two:
Young PETER GRAY, who tasted teas for BAKER, CROOP,
          AND CO.,
And SOMERS, who from Eastern shores imported indigo.

These passengers, by reason of their clinging to a mast,
Upon a desert island were eventually cast.   10

128

They hunted for their meals, as ALEXANDER SELKIRK used,
But they couldn't chat together—they had not been intro-
    duced.

For PETER GRAY and SOMERS too, though certainly in trade,
Were properly particular about the friends they made;
And somehow thus they settled it without a word of mouth—
That GRAY should take the northern half, while SOMERS took
    the south.

On PETER'S portion oysters grew—a delicacy rare,
But oysters were a delicacy PETER couldn't bear.
On SOMERS' side was turtle, on the shingle lying thick,
Which SOMERS couldn't eat, because it always made him
    sick.   20

GRAY gnashed his teeth with envy as he saw a mighty store
Of turtle unmolested on his fellow-creature's shore.
The oysters at his feet aside impatiently he shoved,
For turtle and his mother were the only things he loved.

And SOMERS sighed in sorrow as he settled in the south,
For the thought of PETER'S oysters brought the water to his
    mouth.
He longed to lay him down upon the shelly bed, and stuff:
He had often eaten oysters, but had never had enough.

How they wished an introduction to each other they had had
When on board the *Ballyshannon*! And it drove them nearly
    mad   30
To think how very friendly with each other they might get,
If it wasn't for the arbitrary rule of etiquette!

One day, when out a-hunting for the *mus ridiculus*,
GRAY overheard his fellow-man soliloquizing thus:

129

"I wonder how the playmates of my youth are getting on,
M'CONNELL, S. B. WALTERS, PADDY BYLES, and ROBINSON?"

These simple words made PETER as delighted as could be,
Old chummies at the Charterhouse were ROBINSON and he!
He walked straight up to SOMERS, then he turned extremely
    red,
Hesitated, hummed and hawed a bit, then cleared his throat,
    and said: 40

"I beg your pardon—pray forgive me if I seem too bold,
But you have breathed a name I knew familiarly of old.
You spoke aloud of ROBINSON—I happened to be by.
You know him?" "Yes, extremely well." "Allow me, so
    do I."

It was enough: they felt they could more pleasantly get on,
For (ah, the magic of the fact!) they each knew ROBINSON!
And MR. SOMERS' turtle was at PETER'S service quite,
And MR. SOMERS punished PETER'S oyster-beds all night.

They soon became like brothers from community of wrongs:
They wrote each other little odes and sang each other
    songs;   50
They told each other anecdotes disparaging their wives;
On several occasions, too, they saved each other's lives.

They felt quite melancholy when they parted for the night,
And got up in the morning soon as ever it was light;
Each other's pleasant company they reckoned so upon,
And all because it happened that they both knew ROBINSON!

They lived for many years on that inhospitable shore,
And day by day they learned to love each other more and
    more.

At last, to their astonishment, on getting up one day,
They saw a frigate anchored in the offing of the bay. 60

To PETER an idea occurred. "Suppose we cross the main?
So good an opportunity may not be found again."
And SOMERS thought a minute, then ejaculated, "Done!
I wonder how my business in the City's getting on."

"But stay," said MR. PETER: "when in England, as you know,
I earned a living tasting teas for BAKER, CROOP, AND CO.,
I may be superseded—my employers think me dead!"
"Then come with me," said SOMERS, "and taste indigo
    instead."

But all their plans were scattered in a moment when they
    found
The vessel was a convict ship from Portland, outward
    bound; 70
When a boat came off to fetch them, though they felt it
    very kind,
To go on board they firmly but respectfully declined.

As both the happy settlers roared with laughter at the joke,
They recognized a gentlemanly fellow pulling stroke:
'Twas ROBINSON—a convict, in an unbecoming frock!
Condemned to seven years for misappropriating stock!!!

They laughed no more, for SOMERS thought he had been
    rather rash
In knowing one whose friend had misappropriated cash;
And PETER thought a foolish tack he must have gone upon
In making the acquaintance of a friend of ROBINSON. 80

At first they didn't quarrel very openly, I've heard;
They nodded when they met, and now and then exchanged
    a word:

131

The word grew rare, and rarer still the nodding of the head,
And when they meet each other now, they cut each other dead.

To allocate the island they agreed by word of mouth,
And PETER takes the north again, and SOMERS takes the south;
And PETER has the oysters, which he hates, in layers thick,
And SOMERS has the turtle—turtle always makes him sick.

SIR W. S. GILBERT

"KILMENY"

Dark, dark lay the drifters against the red West,
    As they shot their long meshes of steel overside;
And the oily green waters were rocking to rest
    When *Kilmeny* went out, at the turn of the tide.
And nobody knew where that lassie would roam,
    For the magic that called her was tapping unseen.
It was well-nigh a week ere *Kilmeny* came home,
    And nobody knew where *Kilmeny* had been.

She'd a gun at her bow that was Newcastle's best,
    And a gun at her stern that was fresh from the
        Clyde,   10
And a secret her skipper had never confessed,
    Not even at dawn, to his newly-wed bride;
And a wireless that whispered above, like a gnome,
    The laughter of London, the boasts of Berlin.
Oh, it may have been mermaids that lured her from
    home,
    But nobody knew where *Kilmeny* had been.

It was dark when *Kilmeny* came home from her quest,
  With her bridge dabbled red where her skipper had
      died;
But she moved like a bride with a rose at her breast;
  And "Well done, *Kilmeny*!" the admiral cried.   20
Now at sixty-four fathom a conger may come,
  And nose at the bones of a drowned submarine;
But late in the evening *Kilmeny* came home,
  And nobody knew where *Kilmeny* had been.

There's a wandering shadow that stares at the foam,
  Though they sing all the night to old England, their
      queen.
Late, late in the evening, *Kilmeny* came home,
  And nobody knew where *Kilmeny* had been.

ALFRED NOYES

THE SLAVE'S DREAM

Beside the ungathered rice he lay,
  His sickle in his hand;
His breast was bare, his matted hair
  Was buried in the sand.
Again, in the mist and shadow of sleep,
  He saw his Native Land.

Wide through the landscape of his dreams
  The lordly Niger flowed;
Beneath the palm trees on the plain
  Once more a king he strode;   10
And heard the tinkling caravans
  Descend the mountain road.

133

He saw once more his dark-eyed queen
    Among her children stand;
They clasped his neck, they kissed his cheeks,
    They held him by the hand!—
A tear burst from the sleeper's lids
    And fell into the sand.

And then at furious speed he rode
    Along the Niger's bank;   20
His bridle-reins were golden chains,
    And, with a martial clank,
At each leap he couldl feel his scabbard of steel
    Smiting his stallion's flank.

Before him, like a blood-red flag,
    The bright flamingoes flew;
From morn till night he followed their flight,
    O'er plains where the tamarind grew,
Till he saw the roofs of Caffre huts,
    And the ocean rose to view.   30

At night he heard the lion roar,
    And the hyena scream,
And the river-horse, as he crushed the reeds
    Beside some hidden stream;
And it passed like a glorious roll of drums,
    Through the triumph of his dream.

The forests, with their myriad tongues,
    Shouted of liberty;
And the Blast of the Desert cried aloud,
    With a voice so wild and free,   40
That he started in his sleep and smiled
    At their tempestuous glee.

He did not feel the driver's whip,
    Nor the burning heat of day;

For Death had illumined the Land of Sleep,
　　And his lifeless body lay
　A worn-out fetter, that the soul
　　Had broken and thrown away!

Henry Wadsworth Longfellow

A BALLAD OF JOHN SILVER

We were schooner-rigged and rakish, with a long and lissome
　　hull,
And we flew the pretty colours of the cross-bones and the
　　skull;
We'd a big black Jolly Roger flapping grimly at the fore,
And we sailed the Spanish Water in the happy days of yore.

We'd a long brass gun amidships, like a well-conducted ship,
We had each a brace of pistols and a cutlass at the hip;
It's a point which tells against us, and a fact to be deplored,
But we chased the goodly merchantmen and laid their ships
　　aboard.

Then the dead men fouled the scuppers and the wounded
　　filled the chains,
And the paint-work all was spatter-dashed with other
　　people's brains,　　　　　　　　　　　　　　　　　10
She was boarded, she was looted, she was scuttled till she
　　sank,
And the pale survivors left us by the medium of the plank.

O! then it was (while standing by the taffrail on the poop)
We could hear the drowning folk lament the absent chicken-
　　coop;
Then, having washed the blood away, we'd little else to do
Than to dance a quiet hornpipe as the old salts taught us to.

O! the fiddle on the fo'c's'le, and the slapping naked soles,
And the genial "Down the middle, Jake, and curtsey when
    she rolls!"
With the silver seas around us and the pale moon overhead,
And the look-out not a-looking and his pipe-bowl glowing
    red.   20

Ah! the pig-tailed, quidding pirates and the pretty pranks
    we played,
All have since been put a stop to by the naughty Board of
    Trade;
The schooners and the merry crews are laid away to rest,
A little south the sunset in the Islands of the Blest.

JOHN MASEFIELD

DANIEL WEBSTER'S HORSES

If when the wind blows
Rattling the trees
Clicking like skeletons'
Elbows and knees,

You hear along the road
Three horses pass—
Do not go near the dark
Cold window glass.

If when the first snow lies
Whiter than bones   10
You see the mark of hoofs
Cut to the stones,

Hoofs of three horses
Going abreast—

136

Turn about, turn about,
A closed door is best!

Upright in the earth
Under the sod
They buried three horses
Bridled and shod,   **20**

Daniel Webster's horses—
He said as he grew old,
"Flesh, I loved riding,
Shall I not love it, cold?

"Shall I not love to ride
Bone astride bone,
When the cold wind blows
And snow covers stone?

"Bury them on their feet
With bridle and bit.   **30**
They were fine horses—
See their shoes fit."

ELIZABETH COATSWORTH

ON THE WAY TO THE MISSION

They dogged him all one afternoon,
Through the bright snow,
Two whitemen servants of greed;
He knew that they were there,
But he turned not his head;
He was an Indian trapper;
He planted his snow-shoes firmly;
He dragged the long toboggan
Without rest.

137

The three figures drifted   10
Like shadows in the mind of a seer;
The snow-shoes were whisperers
On the threshold of awe;
The toboggan made the sound of wings,
A wood-pigeon sloping to her nest.

The Indian's face was calm.
He strode with the sorrow of fore-knowledge,
But his eyes were jewels of content
Set in circles of peace.

They would have shot him;   20
But momently in the deep forest,
They saw something flit by his side;
Their hearts stopped with fear.
Then the moon rose.
They would have left him to the spirit,
But they saw the long toboggan
Rounded well with furs,
With many a silver fox-skin,
With the pelts of mink and of otter.

They were the servants of greed;   30
When the moon grew brighter
And the spruces were dark with sleep,
They shot him.
When he fell on a shield of moonlight
One of his arms clung to his burden;
The snow was not melted:
The spirit passed away.

Then the servants of greed
Tore off the cover to count their gains;
They shuddered away into the shadows,   40

Hearing each the loud heart of the other.
Silence was born.

There in the tender moonlight,
   As sweet as they were in life,
Glimmered the ivory features,
   Of the Indian's wife.

In the manner of Montagnais women
   Her hair was rolled with braid;
Under her waxen fingers
   A crucifix was laid.   50

He was drawing her down to the Mission,
   To bury her there in spring,
When the bloodroot comes and the windflower
   To silver everything.

But as a gift of plunder
   Side by side were they laid,
The moon went on to her setting
   And covered them with shade.

DUNCAN CAMPBELL SCOTT

THE QUAKER'S MEETING

A traveller wended the wilds among,
With a purse of gold and a silver tongue;
His hat it was broad, and all drab were his clothes,
For he hated high colours—except on his nose,
And he met with a lady, the story goes
   Heigho! *yea* thee and *nay* thee.

139

The damsel she cast him a merry blink,
And the traveller nothing was loth, I think;
Her merry black eye beamed her bonnet beneath,
And the Quaker, he grinned, for he'd very good teeth, 10
And he asked, "Art thee going to ride on the heath?"

"I hope you'll protect me, kind sir," said the maid,
"As to ride this heath over, I'm sadly afraid;
For robbers, they say, here in numbers abound,
And I wouldn't for anything I should be found,
For, between you and me, I have five hundred pound."

"If that is thy own, dear," the Quaker, he said,
"I ne'er saw a maiden I sooner would wed;
And I have another five hundred just now,
In the padding that's under my saddle-bow,   20
And I'll settle it all upon thee, I vow!"

The maiden she smiled, and her rein she drew,
"Your offer I'll take, but I'll not take you."
A pistol she held at the Quaker's head—
"Now give me your gold, or I'll give you my lead,
'Tis under the saddle, I think you said."

The damsel she ripped up the saddle-bow,
And the Quaker was never a quaker till now!
And he saw, by the fair one he wished for a bride,
His purse borne away with a swaggering stride,   30
And the eye that shammed tender, now only defied.

"The spirit doth move me, friend Broadbrim," quoth
    she,
"To take all this filthy temptation from thee,
For Mammon deceiveth, and beauty is fleeting,
Accept from thy maiden this right-loving greeting,
For much doth she profit by this Quaker's meeting!

140

"And hark! jolly Quaker, so rosy and sly,
Have righteousness, more than a wench, in thine eye;
Don't go again peeping girls' bonnets beneath,
Remember the one that you met on the heath,   40
Her name's Jimmy Barlow, I tell to your teeth."

"Friend James," quoth the Quaker, "pray listen to me,
For thou canst confer a great favour, d'ye see;
The gold thou hast taken is not mine, my friend,
But my master's; and truly on thee I depend,
To make it appear I my trust did defend.

"So fire a few shots through my clothes, here and there,
To make it appear 'twas a desp'rate affair."
So Jim he popped first through the skirt of his coat,
And then through his collar — quite close to his
          throat;   50
"Now one through my broadbrim," quoth Ephraim,
     "I vote."

"I have but a brace," said bold Jim, "and they're spent,
And I won't load again, for a make-believe rent."—
"Then!"—said Ephraim, producing his pistols, "just
     give
My five hundred pounds back, or, as sure as you live,
I'll make of your body a riddle or sieve."

Jim Barlow was diddled—and, though he was game,
He saw Ephraim's pistol so deadly in aim,
That he gave up the gold, and he took to his scrapers,
And when the whole story got into the papers,   60
They said that "*the thieves were no match for the
     Quakers.*"
     Heigho! *yea* thee and *nay* thee.

SAMUEL LOVER

141

THE TWA CORBIES

As I was walking all alane,
I heard twa corbies making a mane;
The tane unto the t'other say,
"Where sall we gang and dine today?"

"In behint yon auld fail dyke,
I wot there lies a new-slain knight;
And naebody kens that he lies there,
But his hawk, his hound, and lady fair.

"His hound is to the hunting gane,
His hawk to fetch the wild-fowl hame,   **10**
His lady's ta'en another mate,
So we may make our dinner sweet.

"Ye'll sit on his white hause-bane,
And I'll pike out his bonny blue eyne;
Wi' ae lock o' his gowden hair,
We'll theek our nest when it grows bare.

"Mony a one for him makes mane,
But nane sall ken where he is gane;
O'er his white banes, when they are bare,
The wind sall blaw for evermair."   **20**

AUTHOR UNKNOWN

THE SHOOTING OF DAN McGREW

A bunch of the boys were whooping it up in the Malamute
saloon;
The kid that handles the music-box was hitting a jag-time
tune;
Back of the bar, in a solo game, sat Dangerous Dan McGrew,
And watching his luck was his light-o'-love, the lady that's
known as Lou.
When out of the night, which was fifty below, and into the
din and the glare,
There stumbled a miner fresh from the creeks, dog-dirty,
and loaded for bear.
He looked like a man with a foot in the grave and scarcely
the strength of a louse,
Yet he tilted a poke of dust on the bar, and he called for
drinks for the house.
There was none could place the stranger's face, though we
searched ourselves for a clue;
But we drank his health, and the last to drink was Dangerous
Dan McGrew.   **10**

There's men that somehow just grip your eyes, and hold them
hard like a spell;
And such was he, and he looked to me like a man who had
lived in hell;
With a face most hair, and the dreary stare of a dog whose
day is done,
As he watered the green stuff in his glass, and the drops fell
one by one.
Then I got to figgering who he was, and wondering what he'd
do,
And I turned my head—and there watching him was the
lady that's known as Lou.

His eyes went rubbering round the room, and he seemed in a kind of daze,

Till at last that old piano fell in the way of his wandering gaze.

The rag-time kid was having a drink; there was no one else on the stool,

So the stranger stumbles across the room, and flops down there like a fool. 20

In a buckskin shirt that was glazed with dirt he sat, and I saw him sway;

Then he clutched the keys with his talon hands—my God! but that man could play.

Were you ever out in the Great Alone, when the moon was awful clear,

And the icy mountains hemmed you in with a silence you most could *hear*;

With only the howl of a timber-wolf, and you camped there in the cold,

A half-dead thing in a stark, dead world, clean mad for the muck called gold;

While high overhead, green, yellow and red, the North Lights swept in bars?—

Then you've a hunch what the music meant . . . hunger and night and the stars.

And hunger not of the belly kind, that's banished with bacon and beans,

But the gnawing hunger of lonely men for a home and all that it means; 30

For a fireside far from the cares that are, four walls and a roof above;

But oh! so cramful of cozy joy, and crowned with a woman's love—

144

A woman dearer than all the world, and true as Heaven is
  true—
(God! how ghastly she looks through her rouge,—the lady
  that's known as Lou.)

Then on a sudden the music changed, so soft that you scarce
  could hear;
But you felt that your life had been looted clean of all that
  it once held dear;
That someone had stolen the woman you loved; that her
  love was a devil's lie;
That your guts were gone, and the best for you was to crawl
  away and die.
'Twas the crowning cry of a heart's despair, and it thrilled
  you through and through—
"I guess I'll make it a spread misere," said Dangerous Dan
  McGrew.   40

The music almost died away . . . then it burst like a pent-up
  flood;
And it seemed to say, "Repay, repay," and my eyes were
  blind with blood.
The thought came back of an ancient wrong, and it stung
  like a frozen lash,
And the lust awoke to kill, to kill . . . then the music stopped
  with a crash,
And the stranger turned, and his eyes they burned in a most
  peculiar way;
In a buckskin shirt that was glazed with dirt he sat, and I
  saw him sway;
Then his lips went in in a kind of grin, and he spoke, and his
  voice was calm,
And "Boys," says he, "you don't know me, and none of you
  care a damn;

145

But I want to state, and my words are straight, and I'll bet
    my poke they're true,
That one of you is a hound of hell . . . and that one is Dan
    McGrew."   50

Then I ducked my head, and the lights went out, and two
    guns blazed in the dark,
And a woman screamed, and the lights went up, and two men
    lay stiff and stark.
Pitched on his head, and pumped full of lead, was Dangerous
    Dan McGrew,
While the man from the creeks lay clutched to the breast
    of the lady that's known as Lou.

These are the simple facts of the case, and I guess I ought
    to know.
They say that the stranger was crazed with "hooch", and
    I'm not denying it's so.
I'm not so wise as the lawyer guys, but strictly between us
    two—
The woman that kissed him—and pinched his poke—was
    the lady that's known as Lou.

ROBERT W. SERVICE

CHRISTMAS AT SEA

The sheets were frozen hard, and they cut the naked hand;
The decks were like a slide, where a seaman scarce could
    stand,
The wind was a nor'wester, blowing squally off the sea;
And cliffs and spouting breakers were the only things a-lee.

We heard the surf a-roaring before the break of day;
But 'twas only with the peep of light we saw how ill we lay.
We tumbled every hand on deck instanter, with a shout,
And we gave her the maintops'l, and stood by to go about.

All day we tacked and tacked between the South Head and
    the North;
All day we hauled the frozen sheets, and got no further
    forth;   10
All day as cold as charity, in bitter pain and dread,
For very life and nature we tacked from head to head.

We gave the South a wider berth, for there the tide-race
    roared;
But every tack we made we brought the North Head close
    aboard;
So's we saw the cliffs and houses, and the breakers running
    high,
And the coastguard in his garden, with his glass against his
    eye.

The frost was on the village roofs as white as ocean foam;
The good red fires were burning bright in every long-shore
    home;
The windows sparkled clear, and the chimneys volleyed out;
And I vow we sniffed the victuals as the vessel went about. 20

The bells upon the church were rung with a mighty jovial
    cheer;
For it's just that I should tell you how (of all days in the
    year)
This day of our adversity was blessed Christmas morn,
And the house above the coastguard's was the house where
    I was born.

Oh, well I saw the pleasant room, the pleasant faces there,
My mother's silver spectacles, my father's silver hair;

And well I saw the firelight, like a flight of homely elves
Go dancing round the china plates that stand upon the
shelves!

And well I knew the talk they had, the talk that was of me,
Of the shadow on the household and the son that went to
sea;   30
And oh, the wicked fool I seemed, in every kind of way,
To be here and hauling frozen ropes on blessed Christmas
Day.

They lit the high sea light, and the dark began to fall.
"All hands to loose topgallant sails!" I heard the captain
call.
"By the Lord, she'll never stand it," our first mate Jackson
cried.
. . . "It's the one way or the other, Mr. Jackson," he replied.

She staggered to her bearings, but the sails were new and
good,
And the ship smelt up to windward just as though she understood.
As the winter's day was ending, in the entry of the night,
We cleared the weary headland, and passed below the
light.   40

And they heaved a mighty breath, every soul on board but
me,
As they saw her nose again pointing handsome out to sea;
But all that I could think of, in the darkness and the cold,
Was just that I was leaving home and my folks were growing
old.

ROBERT LOUIS STEVENSON

148

ROBIN HOOD AND ALAN A DALE

Come listen to me, you gallants so free,
  All you that love mirth for to hear,
And I will you tell of a bold outláw,
  That lived in Nottinghamshire.

As Robin Hood in the forest stood,
  All under the greenwood tree,
There was he ware of a brave young man,
  As fine as fine might be.

The youngster was clothed in scarlet red,
  In scarlet fine and gay,   10
And he did frisk it over the plain,
  And chanted a roundelay.

As Robin Hood next morning stood,
  Amongst the leaves so gay,
There did he espy the same young man
  Come drooping along the way.

The scarlet he wore the day before,
  It was clean cast away;
And every step he fetched a sigh,
  "Alack and a well a day!"   20

Then steppèd forth brave Little John,
  And Much the miller's son,
Which made the young man bend his bow,
  When as he saw them come.

"Stand off, stand off!" the young man said,
  "What is your will with me?"—

"You must come before our master straight,
    Under yon greenwood tree."

And when he came bold Robin before,
    Robin asked him courteously,   30
"O hast thou any money to spare,
    For my merry men and me?"

"I have no money," the young man said,
    "But five shillings and a ring;
And that I have kept this seven long years,
    To have it at my wedding.

"Yesterday I should have married a maid,
    But she is now from me ta'en,
And chosen to be an old knight's delight,
    Whereby my poor heart is slain."   40

"What is thy name?" then said Robin Hood,
    "Come tell me, without any fail."—
"By the faith of my body," then said the young
        man,
    "My name it is Alan a Dale."

"What wilt thou give me," said Robin Hood,
    "In ready gold or fee,
To help thee to thy true-love again,
    And deliver her unto thee?"

"I have no money," then quoth the young man,
    "No ready gold nor fee,   50
But I will swear upon a book
    Thy true servant for to be."—

"But how many miles to thy true-love?
    Come tell me without any guile."—

"By the faith of my body," then said the young
    man,
  "It is but five little mile."

Then Robin he hasted over the plain,
  He did neither stint nor lin,
Until he came unto the church
  Where Alan should keep his wedding.   **60**

"What dost thou do here?" the Bishop he said,
  "I prithee now to tell to me."
"I am a bold harper," quoth Robin Hood,
  "And the best in the north country."

"O welcome, O welcome!" the Bishop he said,
  "That music best pleaseth me."—
"You shall have no music," quoth Robin Hood,
  "Till the bride and the bridegroom I see."

With that came in a wealthy knight,
  Which was both grave and old,   **70**
And after him a finikin lass,
  Did shine like glistering gold.

"This is no fit match," quoth bold Robin Hood,
  "That you do seem to make here;
For since we are come unto the church,
  The bride she shall choose her own dear."

Then Robin Hood put his horn to his mouth,
  And blew blasts two or three;
When four and twenty bowmen bold
  Come leaping over the lea.   **80**

And when they came into the churchyard,
  Marching all on a row,

151

The first man was Alan a Dale,
　　To give bold Robin his bow.

"This is thy true-love," Robin he said,
　　"Young Alan, as I hear say;
And you shall be married at this same time,
　　Before we depart away."

"That shall not be," the Bishop he said,
　　"For thy word it shall not stand;　　　90
They shall be three times asked in the church,
　　As the law is of our land."

Robin Hood pulled off the Bishop's coat,
　　And put it upon Little John;
"By the faith of my body," then Robin said,
　　"The cloth doth make thee a man."

When Little John went into the choir,
　　The people began for to laugh;
He asked them seven times in the church,
　　Lest three should not be enough.　　　100

"Who gives me this maid?" then said Little John.
　　Quoth Robin, "That do I!
And he that doth take her from Alan a Dale
　　Full dearly he shall her buy."

And thus having ended this merry wedding,
　　The bride looked as fresh as a queen,
And so they returned to the merry greenwood,
　　Amongst the leaves so green.

AUTHOR UNKNOWN

PAUL BUNYAN

He came
striding
over the mountain,
the moon slung on his back,
like a pack.
A great pine,
stuck on his shoulder,
swayed as he walked,
as he talked
to his blue ox   10
Babe;
a huge, looming shadow
of a man,
clad
in a mackinaw coat,
his logger's shirt
open at the throat
and the great mane of hair
matching,
meeting   20
the locks of night,
the smoke from his cauldron pipe
a cloud on the moon;
and his laugh
rolled through the mountains
like thunder
on a summer night
while the lightning of his smile
split the heavens
asunder.   30
His blue ox, Babe,

153

pawed the ground
till the earth
trembled
and shook
and a high cliff
toppled and fell;
and Babe's bellow
was fellow
to the echo   40
of Bunyan's laughter;
and then
with one step
he was in the next valley
dragging the moon after,
the stars
tangled,
spangled
in the branches of the great pine.
And as he left,   50
he whistled in the dark
like a far-off train
blowing for a crossing,
and plainly heard
were the plodding grunts
of Babe, the blue ox,
trying
to keep pace
from hill to hill,
and then, the sounds,   60
fading,
dying,
were lost
in the churn of night,—
and all was still.

ARTHUR STANLEY BOURINOT

154

THE CALF PATH

One day, through the primeval wood,
A calf walked home as good calves should;
But made a trail all bent askew,
A crooked trail as all calves do.

Since then two hundred years have fled,
And I infer the calf is dead.
But still he left behind his trail,
And thereby hangs my moral tale.

The trail was taken up next day
By a lone dog that passed that way;   10
And then a wise bell-wether sheep,
Pursued the trail o'er vale and steep,
And drew the flock behind him, too,
As good bell-wethers always do.

And from that day o'er hill and glade,
Through these old woods a path was made;
And many men wound in and out,
And dodged and turned and bent about,
And uttered words of righteous wrath
Because 'twas such a crooked path.   20
But still they followed—do not laugh—
The first migrations of that calf,
And through this winding wood-way stalked
Because he wobbled when he walked.

This forest path became a lane
That bent, and turned, and turned again;
This crooked lane became a road,

Where many a poor horse with his load
Toiled on beneath the burning sun,
And travelled some three miles in one.   30
    And thus a century and a half
    They trod the footsteps of that calf.

The years passed on in swiftness fleet,
The road became a village street;
    And this, before men were aware,
    A city's crowded thoroughfare;
And soon the central street was this
Of a renowned metropolis;
    And men two centuries and a half
    Trod in the footsteps of that calf.   40

Each day a hundred thousand rout
Followed the zigzag calf about;
    And o'er his crooked journey went
    The traffic of a continent.
A hundred thousand men were led
By one calf near three centuries dead;
    They followed still his crooked way,
    And lost one hundred years a day;
For thus such reverence is lent
To a well-established precedent.   50

But how the wise old wood-gods laugh
Who saw the first primeval calf!
And many things this tale might teach—
But I am not ordained to preach.

SAM WALTER FOSS

THE HIGHWAYMAN

Part I

The wind was a torrent of darkness among the gusty trees,
The moon was a ghostly galleon tossed upon cloudy seas.
The road was a ribbon of moonlight over the purple moor,
And the highwayman came riding—
       Riding—riding—
The highwayman came riding, up to the old inn-door.

He'd a French cocked-hat on his forehead, a bunch of lace
    at his chin,
A coat of the claret velvet, and breeches of brown doe-skin.
They fitted with never a wrinkle. His boots were up to the
    thigh.
And he rode with a jewelled twinkle,   10
       His pistol butts a-twinkle,
His rapier hilt a-twinkle, under the jewelled sky.

Over the cobbles he clattered and clashed in the dark inn-
    yard.
He tapped with his whip on the shutters, but all was locked
    and barred.
He whistled a tune to the window, and who should be wait-
    ing there
But the landlord's black-eyed daughter,
       Bess, the landlord's daughter,
Plaiting a dark red love-knot into her long black hair.

And dark in the dark old inn-yard a stable-wicket creaked
Where Tim the ostler listened. His face was white and
    peaked.   20
His eyes were hollows of madness, his hair like mouldy hay,

But he loved the landlord's daughter,
       The landlord's red-lipped daughter.
Dumb as a dog he listened, and he heard the robber say—

"One kiss, my bonny sweetheart, I'm after a prize tonight,
But I shall be back with the yellow gold before the morning
       light;
Yet if they press me sharply, and harry me through the day,
Then look for me by moonlight,
       Watch for me by moonlight,
I'll come to thee by moonlight, though hell should bar the
       way."   30

He rose upright in the stirrups. He scarce could reach her
       hand,
But she loosened her hair i' the casement. His face burnt
       like a brand
As the black cascade of perfume came tumbling over his
       breast;
And he kissed its waves in the moonlight,
       (Oh, sweet black waves in the moonlight!)
Then he tugged at his rein in the moonlight, and galloped
       away to the west.

Part II

He did not come in the dawning. He did not come at noon;
And out o' the tawny sunset, before the rise o' the moon,
When the road was a gipsy's ribbon, looping the purple moor,
A red-coat troop came marching—   40
       Marching—marching—
King George's men came marching, up to the old inn-door.

They said no word to the landlord. They drank his ale
       instead.
But they gagged his daughter, and bound her, to the foot of
       her narrow bed.

158

Two of them knelt at her casement, with muskets at their
    side!
There was death at every window;
        And hell at one dark window;
For Bess could see, through her casement, the road that *he*
    would ride.

They had tied her up to attention, with many a sniggering
    jest.
They had bound a musket beside her, with the muzzle be-
    neath her breast!   50
"Now, keep good watch!" and they kissed her.
        She heard the dead man say—
Look for me by moonlight;
       Watch for me by moonlight;
I'll come to thee by moonlight, though hell should bar the
    way!

She twisted her hands behind her; but all the knots held good!
She writhed her hands till her fingers were wet with sweat or
    blood!
They stretched and strained in the darkness, and the hours
    crawled by like years,
Till, now, on the stroke of midnight,
        Cold, on the stroke of midnight,   60
The tip of one finger touched it! The trigger at least was
    hers!

The tip of one finger touched it. She strove no more for the
    rest.
Up, she stood up to attention, with the muzzle beneath her
    breast.
She would not risk their hearing; she would not strive again;
For the road lay bare in the moonlight;
        Blank and bare in the moonlight;
And the blood of her veins, in the moonlight, throbbed to
    her love's refrain.

Tlot-tlot; tlot-tlot! Had they heard it? The horse-hoofs ringing clear;
Tlot-tlot, tlot-tlot, in the distance? Were they deaf that they did not hear?
Down the ribbon of moonlight, over the brow of the hill, 70
The highwayman came riding,
         Riding, riding!
The red-coats looked to their priming! She stood up, straight and still.

Tlot-tlot, in the frosty silence! *Tlot-tlot*, in the echoing night!
Nearer he came and nearer. Her face was like a light.
Her eyes grew wide for a moment; she drew one last deep breath,
Then her finger moved in the moonlight,
         Her musket shattered the moonlight,
Shattered her breast in the moonlight and warned him—with her death.

He turned. He spurred to the westward; he did not know who stood 80
Bowed, with her head o'er the musket, drenched with her own red blood!
Not till the dawn he heard it, and his face grew grey to hear
How Bess, the landlord's daughter,
         The landlord's black-eyed daughter,
Had watched for her love in the moonlight, and died in the darkness there.

Back, he spurred like a madman, shouting a curse to the sky,
With the white road smoking behind him and his rapier brandished high.
Blood-red were his spurs i' the golden noon; wine-red was his velvet coat;
When they shot him down on the highway,

160

Down like a dog on the highway, 90
And he lay in his blood on the highway, with the bunch of
lace at his throat.

*And still of a winter's night, they say, when the wind is in
the trees,*
When the moon is a ghostly galleon tossed upon cloudy seas,
*When the road is a ribbon of moonlight over the purple
moor,*
A highwayman comes riding—
Riding—riding—
A highwayman comes riding, up to the old inn-door.

Over the cobbles he clatters and clangs in the dark inn-yard.
*And he taps with his whip on the shutters, but all is locked
and barred.*
*He whistles a tune to the window, and who should be wait-
ing there* 100
But the landlord's black-eyed daughter,
Bess, the landlord's daughter,
Plaiting a dark red love-knot into her long black hair.

ALFRED NOYES

THE "JERVIS BAY" GOES DOWN

She is an old freighter
Of some fourteen thousand tons,
Standing in the roadstead
Of a port somewhere south of Singapore.
She lists a bit,
As if wearied by the typhoons of the China Seas;
By the whole gales of Tasman;
By the turbulence of wind off Borneo.

Her gear is obsolete,
Her iron skin blistered,   10
Pocked with rust.
Her engines are rheumatic,
And her saw-tooth screw
Will yield less than fourteen knots . . .
She is the old *Jervis Bay*
Of Australian registry,
Resting, between tides, from her
Obscure drudgeries,
Somewhere south of Singapore.
She nods at her mooring cables,
Head bent to the dry monsoon.   20
The *Jervis Bay* is nodding, half asleep,
When a gig draws alongside,
And there is brought aboard,
Solemnly, a flag with a blue field—
A storied ensign — emblem of Britain's Naval
            Reserve.
This of itself becomes a rousing circumstance
To one so frowsed, so drably sleeping,
Somewhere south of Singapore.

Up the starboard ladder-way
There comes a new master,   30
Puffing somewhat with middle age.
He looks about, he looks above, below.
Forward, aft he peers.
His is the manner of a man recapturing a
            memory.
He is Fogarty Feegan,
Called from retirement
To command the *Jervis Bay*.
For ten years Fogarty Feegan
Has walked in his English garden,
Watching the roses bud, the violets bloom,   40
Enjoying each miracle of season

162

That brings white blossoms to the hawthorn
hedge.
But now he has left his barrow and his slips
To bring the storied ensign, with its blue field—
Blue as the violets of his garden—
Bringing it from afar to the old *Jervis Bay*.

His voice rolls against the breakwater.
His big hands grasp the teakwood rail.
He swears a bit, and finally
The *Jervis Bay* awakens.   50
Soon a battery is supplied—
A small one—
Guns of five-inch calibre.
Then, with a hundred young reservists for her
crew,
The *Jervis Bay* puts out to sea,
From somewhere south of Singapore.

Captain Fogarty Feegan
Has a distant rendezvous
With other old masters,
Summoned from retirement,   60
Called by their King
   From their little farms,
   From their office stools,
   From their fireside chairs,
   From the cities and the shires—
For threefold war—earth, sky, sea—
Beggars the world.
Ships go down . . . each day go down,
And bottoms must be had
To bear cargoes to Britain.   70

Now up comes the *Jervis Bay*,
Up from tropical waters,
Through Suez, through the Strait of Gibraltar,

Out and across the Atlantic,
And to the Americas.
In a harbour of the North,
And with brave haste, the old hulls
Are laden to their loading lines
With cargoes for Britain.
Captain Fogarty Feegan   80
Listens to the rumbling of winches;
Hears the samson posts creak;
Hears the chains and blocks complain;
Harries his First Officer, Mr. Wilson, with
        commands,
As things needful for the life-beat
Of England's great heart
Are stowed aboard.
"Hurry, damme, Mr. Wilson, sir!"
He shouts to his First Officer.
"We are not sleeping now, Mr. Wilson,   90
Somewhere south of Singapore!"

From a Canadian bay,
From behind the fog-bank of November dawn,
A convoy line puts out;
Thirty-eight ships put out to sea
With cargoes for Britain,
A consignment to help sustain
The life-beat of England;
Goods to provision an Isle
That for a thousand years   100
Has prized the freedom
And the dignity of Man.
The gun crews of the *Jervis Bay*
Sleep beside their battery.
They seem young seminars
With parka hoods cowling their heads
To keep out the cold sea-rime.

Night falls, a great and sombre hymn.
The night of November fourth—
Nineteen hundred and forty years since Our
    Lord— 110
Is an anthem of wind and small, following sea.
The morning comes like a priest,
Upholding a golden monstrance.
The morning of the fifth
Finds the *Jervis Bay* and her convoy
Strung like a procession of pilgrims against the
    dawn.
The ship's bell sounds;
The practice rounds are fired.
The sun is on the meridian,
And Fogarty Feegan shoots the sun 120
For latitude.
Eight bells again,
And Fogarty Feegan shoots the sun
For longitude.
And then, at five o'clock
The lookout calls from the crow's-nest:
"Ship, sir, off the starboard bow!"

Through his glass,
Fogarty Feegan makes out smoke—
A black gargoyle in the sky— 130
East by south-east,
Then sights a ship, hull down.
And now a battleship
Comes boiling over the horizon.
She opens fire with heavy guns.
Captain Fogarty Feegan telegraphs his engine
    room
To strain the boilers till they burst.
He bellows, curses, brings to bear
The popguns of his battery

Against the Goliath armour of the battleship. 140
He sends up smoke to screen the fleet.
He orders all the convoy ships to scatter wide
    and fast.
Then Fogarty Feegan
Sets out alone to meet the battleship.
Five-inch guns against eleven-inch guns.
Egg-shell hull against Krupp plate.
"Damme, Mr. Wilson, sir," he shouts,
"We're not hearing mandolins today, somewhere
    south of Singapore!"
This is a mad thing to do
This sea-charge of the *Jervis Bay,*   150
Yet a sky of dead admirals looks down
From the Grand Haven,
Looks down at Fogarty Feegan,
Whose senile tub
Steams bow-on for the battleship.
Nelson, Drake, Beatty, Harwood;
Yes, and the Americans:
Porter, Farragut and John Paul Jones,
All look down in wonderment.

And now a burst of shrapnel rakes the *Jervis
    Bay,*   160
And tears the right arm from the sleeve of
    Fogarty Feegan.
He does not fall.
He grasps the teakwood rail with his other hand,
Masking his agony with bellowings that rise
    above the guns.
Nor will he let a tourniquet
Be placed upon the stump.
He waves the stump, and Mr. Wilson knows
(And the sky of dead admirals knows)
That if a hand were there,

166

It would be making a great fist.   **170**
Still steaming toward the battleship,
Fogarty Feegan keeps his little guns ablast.
The eyes of the setters
And of the pointers
Grow black and blue from the recoils—
Their eardrums dead.
A salvo comes with the top roll of the battle-
      ship.
And now the ensign—
Emblem with the blue field—
Is shot away.   **180**
Enraged, bloody, rocking on his heels,
Fogarty Feegan roars
"Hoist another ensign, damme, Mr. Wilson, sir!
Hoist another flag,
That we may fight like Englishmen!"
A boatswain procures a flag from the locker—
A flag used for the burial of the dead at sea.
"Here, sir," he cries,
As to a brace he bends
The Banner of England.   **190**

The *Jervis Bay*, ablaze from stern to bow,
At dusk, still fires her puny guns,
And will not change her course.
Salvos from turrets,
Guns three-over-three,
Make great geysers grow about
The old ship's wake.
But still her guns give voice.
And now she's struck below the water-line.
Her boilers go.   **200**
The *Jervis Bay* begins to settle by the stern.
Yet, sinking, still she faces her antagonist.
Then the waters begin to close over her.

The waters close over Fogarty Feegan,
And over the flag
That once was used for burials at sea.
And now night spreads its shroud.

Of thirty-eight ships in the convoy,
Twenty-nine are saved,
Their cargoes saved,   210
To help sustain the life-beat of England,
While from the sky dead admirals look on,
And claim Captain Fogarty Feegan for their
     own.

The *Jervis Bay* goes down—
Goes down as no mere casualty of storm,
To rust out, fathoms deep, in common grave
With sisters unremembered by the years.
The *Jervis Bay*—of Australian registry,
From somewhere south of Singapore—
Goes down in the history   220
Of an Isle that for a thousand years
Has prized the freedom
And the dignity of Man.

                              GENE FOWLER

THE DEACON'S MASTERPIECE

Have you heard of the wonderful One-Hoss Shay,
That was built in such a logical way
It ran a hundred years to a day?
And then, of a sudden, it—ah! but stay,
I'll tell you what happened, without delay—
Scaring the parson into fits,

168

Frightening people out of their wits—
Have you ever heard of that, I say?

Seventeen hundred and fifty-five;
Georgius Secundus was then alive—   10
Snuffy old drone from the German hive!—
That was the year when Lisbon town
Saw the earth open and gulp her down;
And Braddock's army was done so brown,
Left without a scalp to its crown.
It was on that terrible Earthquake day
That the Deacon finished the One-Hoss Shay.

Now, in building of chaises, I tell you what,
There is always, *somewhere*, a weakest spot—
In hub, tire, felloe, in spring or thill,   20
In panel or crossbar, or floor, or sill,
In screw, bolt, thorough-brace—lurking still.
Find it somewhere, you must and will—
Above or below, or within or without;
And that's the reason, beyond a doubt,
A chaise *breaks down*, but doesn't *wear out*.

But the Deacon swore (as deacons do,
With an "I dew vum" or an "I tell yeou,")
He would build one shay to beat the taown
'N' the keounty 'n' the kentry raoun';   30
It should be so built that it *couldn'* break daown:
"Fur," said the Deacon, " 'tis mighty plain
Thut the weakes' place mus' stan' the strain;
'N' the way t' fix it, uz I maintain,
              Is only jest
To make that place uz strong uz the rest."

So the Deacon inquired of the village folk
Where he could find the strongest oak,

That couldn't be split, nor bent, nor broke—
That was for spokes and floor and sills;   40
He sent for lancewood to make the thills;
The crossbars were ash, from the straightest trees;
The panels of white-wood, that cuts like cheese,
But lasts like iron for things like these;
The hubs of logs from the "Settler's Ellum",
Last of its timber—they couldn't sell 'em—
Never an axe had seen their chips,
And the wedges flew from between their lips,
Their blunt ends frizzled like celery-tips;
Step and prop-iron, bolt and screw,   50
Spring, tire, axle, and linch-pin too,
Steel of the finest, bright and blue;
Thorough-brace bison-skin, thick and wide;
Boot, top, dasher, from tough old hide,
Found in the pit where the tanner died.
That was the way he "put her through".
"There," said the Deacon, "naow she'll dew!"

Do! I tell you, I rather guess
She was a wonder, and nothing less!
Colts grew horses, beards turned grey,   60
Deacon and deaconess dropped away;
Children and grandchildren—where were they?
But there stood the stout old One-Hoss Shay,
As fresh as on Lisbon Earthquake day!

Eighteen hundred—it came, and found
The Deacon's masterpiece strong and sound.
Eighteen hundred, increased by ten—
"Hahnsum Kerridge" they called it then.
Eighteen hundred and twenty came—
Running as usual—much the same.   70
Thirty and *forty* at last arrive;
And then came *fifty*—and *fifty-five*.

170

Little of all we value here
Wakes on the morn of its hundredth year
Without both feeling and looking queer.
In fact, there's nothing that keeps its youth,
So far as I know, but a tree and truth.
(This is a moral that runs at large;
Take it—you're welcome—no extra charge.)

First of November—the Earthquake day—   80
There are traces of age in the One-Hoss Shay—
A general flavour of mild decay—
But nothing local, as one may say.
There couldn't be, for the Deacon's art
Had made it so like in every part
That there wasn't a chance for one to start.
For the wheels were just as strong as the thills,
And the floor was just as strong as the sills,
And the panels just as strong as the floor,
And the whipple-tree neither less nor more,   90
And the back crossbar as strong as the fore,
And the spring and axle and hub *encore*;
And yet, *as a whole*, it is past a doubt,
In another hour it will be *worn out*!

First of November, 'Fifty-five!
This morning the parson takes a drive.
Now, small boys, get out of the way!
Here comes the wonderful One-Hoss Shay,
Drawn by a rat-tailed, ewe-necked bay.
"Huddup!" said the parson—off went they!   100

The parson was working his Sunday's text;
Had got to *fifthly*, and stopped, perplexed
At what the—Moses—was coming next.
All at once the horse stood still,
Close by the meet'n'-house on the hill:

171

—First a shiver, and then a thrill;
Then something decidedly like a spill;
And the parson was sitting upon a rock,
At half-past nine by the meet'n'-house clock—
Just the hour of the Earthquake shock!   **110**
What do you think the parson found
When he got up and stared around?
The poor old chaise in a heap or mound,
As if it had been to the mill and ground.
You see, of course, if you're not a dunce,
How it went to pieces all at once—
All at once, and nothing first—
Just as bubbles do when they burst.

End of the wonderful One-Hoss Shay!
Logic is *Logic*—that's all I say.   **120**

OLIVER WENDELL HOLMES

THE LIGHTHOUSE

Just as my watch was done, the fog had lifted,
And we could see the flashing of our light,
And see once more the reef beyond the Head
Over which six days and nights the mist had drifted,
Until it seemed all time to mist had drifted
And day and night were but one blind white night.

But on the seventh midnight the wind shifted,
And I was glad to tumble into bed,
Thankful to hear no more the blaring horn
That ceaselessly had sounded, night and morn,   **10**
With moaning echoes through the mist to warn
The blind bewildered ships at sea:

Yet, though as tired as any dog,
I lay awhile and seemed to feel
Fog lying on my eyes still heavily,
And still the horn unceasingly
Sang through my head, till gradually
Through night's strange stillness over me
Sweet sleep began to steal,
Sleep blind and thick and fleecy as the fog.   20

For all I knew, I might have slept
A moment—or eternity,
When, startled by a crash,
I waked to find I'd leapt
Upright on the floor;
And stood there listening to the smash
Of falling glass . . . and then a thud
Of something heavy tumbling
Into the next room . . .
A pad of naked feet . . .   30
A moan . . . a sound of stumbling . . .
A heavier thud . . . and then no more.
And I stood shivering in the gloom,
With creeping flesh and tingling blood,
Until I gave myself a shake
To bring my wits more wide awake,
And lit a lanthorn and flung wide the door.

Half-dazed and dazzled by the light,
At first it seemed I'd only find
A broken pane, a flapping blind;   40
But when I raised the lanthorn o'er my head
I saw a naked boy upon the bed
Who crouched and shuddered on the folded sheet,
And on his face before my feet
A naked man who lay as if quite dead,
Though on his broken knuckles blood was red;

173

And all my wits awakened at the sight.
I set the lanthorn down and took the child,
Who looked at me, with piteous eyes and wild,
And chafed his chill wet body till it glowed,   50
And forcing spirit 'twixt his chattering teeth,
I tucked him snugly in beneath
The blankets and soon left him warmly stowed;
And stooped to tend the man who lay
Still senseless on the floor.
I turned him off his face
And laid him on the other bed,
And washed and staunched his wound;
And yet, for all that I could do,
I could not bring him to,   60
Or see a trace
Of life returning to that heavy head.

It seemed he'd swooned
When through the window he'd made way,
Just having strength to lay
The boy in safety. Still as death
He lay without a breath;
And, seeing I could do no more
To help him in the fight for life,
I turned again to tend the lad,   70
And as I looked on him was glad
To find him sleeping quietly.
So, fetching fuel, I lit a fire
And quickly had as big a blaze
As any housewife could desire:
Then 'twixt the beds I set a chair,
That I might watch until they stirred:
And as I saw them lying there—
The sleeping boy and him who lay
In that strange stiller sleep, 'twas plain   80

174

That they were son and father, now
I'd time to look and wonder how
In such a desperate plight,
Without a stitch or rag,
They'd taken refuge from the night.
And, as I wondered drowsily,
It seemed yet queerer and more queer;
For round the Head the rocks are sheer,
With scarce a foothold for a bird,
And it seemed quite beyond belief   **90**
That any wrecked upon that reef
Could swim ashore and scale the crag
By daylight, let alone by night.

But they who live beside the sea
Know naught's too wonderful to be;
And as I sat and heard
The quiet breathing of the child
Great weariness came over me,
And in a kind of daze
I watched the blaze   **100**
With nodding head,
And must have slept, for presently
I found the man was sitting up in bed,
And talking to himself with wide unseeing eyes.
At first, I hardly made out what he said:
But soon his voice, so hoarse and wild,
Grew calm, and, straining, I could hear
The broken words that came with many sighs.

"Yes, lad: she's going: but there's naught to fear,
For I can swim and tow you in the belt.   **110**
Come, let's join hands together and leap clear. . . .
Ay, son, it's dark and cold . . . but you have felt
The cold and dark before . . .
And you should scorn . . .

175

And we must be near shore . . .
For hark, the horn!
Think of your mother and your home and leap. . . .
She thinks of us, lad, waking or asleep. . . .
You would not leave her lonely?
Nay! . . . then . . . go! . . .   120
Well done, lad! . . . Nay! I'm here. . . .
Ay, son, it's cold: but you're too big to fear.
Now then you're snug: I've got you safe in tow:
The worst is over and we've only
To make for land . . . we've naught . . . to do . . .
    but steer . . .
But steer . . . but steer. . . ."

He paused and sank down in the bed, quite done,
And lay a moment silent, while his son
Still slumbered in the other bed,
And on his quiet face the firelight shone: 130
Then once again the father raised his head
And rambled on. . . .
"Say, lad, what cheer?
I thought you'd dropped asleep, but you're all right.
We'll rest a moment. . . . I'm quite out of breath. . . .
It's farther than . . . Nay, son! there's naught to
    fear . . .
The land must be quite near. . . .
The horn is loud enough!
Only your father's out of puff:
He's getting fat and lazy, is your dad.   140
Ay, lad,
It's cold;
But you're too old
To cry for cold.
Now . . . keep . . . tight hold,
And we'll be off again.
I've got my breath. . . ."

He sank once more still as death,
With hands that clutched the counterpane:
But still the boy was sleeping quietly.   **150**
And then, the father sat up suddenly
And cried *See! See!*
The land! the land!
It's near . . . I touch it with my hand.
And now *Oh God!* he moaned.
Small wonder, when he saw what lay before—
The black unbroken crags so grim and high
That must have seemed to him to soar
Sheer from the sea's edge to the sky.
But soon he plucked up heart, once more: **160**
"We're safe, lad—safe ashore!
A narrow ledge, but land, firm land.
We'll soon be high and dry.
Nay, son, we can't stay here:
The waves would have us back
Or we should perish of the cold,
Come, lad, there's naught to fear. . . .
You must be brave and bold.
Perhaps we'll strike a track.
Ay, son, it's steep, and black   **170**
And slimy to the hold;
But we must climb, and see! the mist is gone:
The stars are shining clear. . . .
Think, son, your mother's at the top,
And you'll be up in no time. See, that star,
The brightest star that ever shone,
Just think it's she who watches you
And knows that you'll be brave and true.
Come, lad, we may not stop . . .
Or, else, the cold . . .   **180**
Give me your hand . . .
Your foot there now . . . just room to stand.
It cannot be so far. . . .

177

We'll soon be up . . . this work should make us
    warm.
Thank God it's not a storm,
Or we should scarce . . . your foot here firm. . . .
Nay, lad! you must not squirm.
Come, be a man: you shall not fall:
I'll hold you tight.
There now you are my own son after all!   190
Your mother, lad,
Her star burns bright . . .
And we're already half-way up the height. . . .
Your mother will be glad,
Ay, she'll be glad to hear
Of her brave boy who had no fear.

Your foot . . . your hand . . . 'twas but a bird
You startled out of bed:
'Twould think it queer
To wake up suddenly and see your head;   200
And when you stirred . . .
Nay! steady, lad!
Or you will send your dad . . .
Your hand . . . your foot . . . we'll rest upon this
    ledge. . . .
Why, son, we're at the top! I feel the edge
And grass—soft dewy grass!
Let go one moment and I'll draw you up. . . .
Now, lad! . . . Thank God that's past! . . .
And you are safe, at last:
You're safe, you're safe . . . and now my precious
    lass   210
Will see her son, her little son, again.

I never thought to reach the top tonight.
God! What a height!

*Nay, but you must not look: 'twould turn your
    head:*
And we must not stand shivering here. . . .
And see! . . . a flashing light. . . .
It's sweeping towards us, and now you stand bright.
Ah, your poor bleeding hands and feet!
My little son, my sweet!
There's nothing more to fear.   220
A lighthouse, lad! And we must make for it.
You're tired; I'll carry you a bit.
Nay, son: 'twill warm me up . . .
And there will be a fire and bed,
And even perhaps a cup
Of something hot to drink,
And something good to eat.
And think, son, only think—
Your home . . . and mother . . . once again!

Once more the weary head   230
Sank back upon the bed;
And for a while he hardly stirred,
But only muttered now and then
A broken word,
As though to cheer
His son who still slept quietly
Upon the other side of me.

And then, my blood ran cold to hear
A sudden cry of fear:
"My son! My son!   240
Ah God, he's done!
I thought I'd laid him on the bed. . . .
I've laid him on white mist instead:
He's fallen sheer. . . ."

179

Then I sprang up and cried: *Your son is here!*
And taking up the sleeping boy
I bore him to his father's arms,
And, as he nestled to his breast,
Kind life came back to those wild eyes
And filled them with deep joy,   250
And free of all alarms
The son and father lay
Together in sweet rest,
While through the window stole the strange clear
    light of day.

WILFRID GIBSON

HORATIUS AT THE BRIDGE

Lars Porsena of Clusium
    By the Nine Gods he swore
That the great house of Tarquin
    Should suffer wrong no more.
By the Nine Gods he swore it,
    And named a trysting day,
And bade his messengers ride forth,
East and west and south and north,
    To summon his array.

East and west and south and north   10
    The messengers ride fast,
And tower and town and cottage
    Have heard the trumpet's blast.
Shame on the false Etruscan
    Who lingers in his home,
When Porsena of Clusium
    Is on the march for Rome.

The horsemen and the footmen
  Are pouring in amain
From many a stately market-place,   20
  From many a fruitful plain,
From many a lonely hamlet
  Which hid by beech and pine,
Like an eagle's nest, hangs on the crest
  Of purple Apennine.

And now hath every city
  Sent up her tale of men;
The foot are fourscore thousand,
  The horse are thousands ten:
Before the gates of Sutrium   30
  Is met the great array.
A proud man was Lars Porsena
  Upon the trysting day.

But by the yellow Tiber
  Was tumult and affright:
From all the spacious champaign
  To Rome men took their flight.
A mile around the city,
  The throng stopped up the ways;
A fearful sight it was to see   40
  Through two long nights and days.

Now, from the rock Tarpeian,
  Could the wan burghers spy
The line of blazing villages
  Red in the midnight sky.
The Fathers of the City,
  They sat all night and day,
For every hour some horseman came
  With tidings of dismay.

I wis, in all the Senate,
    There was no heart so bold,
But sore it ached and fast it beat,
    When that ill news was told.
Forthwith up rose the Consul,
    Up rose the Fathers all;
In haste they girded up their gowns,
    And hied them to the wall.

They held a council standing
    Before the River-Gate;
Short time was there, ye well may guess,   60
    For musing or debate.
Out spake the Consul roundly:
    "The bridge must straight go down;
For, since Janiculum is lost,
    Naught else can save the town."

Just then a scout came flying,
    All wild with haste and fear;
"To arms! to arms! Sir Consul:
    Lars Porsena is here."
On the low hills to westward   70
    The Consul fixed his eye,
And saw the swarthy storm of dust
    Rise fast along the sky.

And nearer fast and nearer
    Doth the red whirlwind come;
And louder still and still more loud,
From underneath that rolling cloud,
Is heard the trumpet's war-note proud,
    The trampling, and the hum.
And plainly and more plainly   80
    Now through the gloom appears,

182

Far to left and far to right,
In broken gleams of dark-blue light,
The long array of helmets bright,
    The long array of spears.

And plainly and more plainly,
    Above that glimmering line,
Now might ye see the banners
    Of twelve fair cities shine;
But the banner of proud Clusium   90
    Was highest of them all,
The terror of the Umbrian,
    The terror of the Gaul.

But the Consul's brow was sad,
    And the Consul's speech was low,
And darkly looked he at the wall,
    And darkly at the foe.
"Their van will be upon us
    Before the bridge goes down;
And if they once may win the bridge,   100
    What hope to save the town?"

Then out spake brave Horatius,
    The Captain of the Gate:
"To every man upon this earth
    Death cometh soon or late.
And how can man die better
    Than facing fearful odds,
For the ashes of his fathers,
    And the temples of his Gods?

"Hew down the bridge, Sir Consul,   110
    With all the speed ye may;
I, with two more to help me,
    Will hold the foe in play.

In yon strait path a thousand
   May well be stopped by three.
Now who will stand on either hand,
   And keep the bridge with me?"

Then out spake Spurius Lartius;
   A Ramnian proud was he:
"Lo, I will stand at thy right hand,   **120**
   And keep the bridge with thee."
And out spake strong Herminius;
   Of Titian blood was he:
"I will abide on thy left side,
   And keep the bridge with thee."

"Horatius," quoth the Consul,
   "As thou sayest, so let it be."
And straight against that great array
   Forth went the dauntless Three.
For Romans in Rome's quarrel   **130**
   Spared neither land nor gold,
Nor son nor wife, nor limb nor life,
   In the brave days of old.

Now while the Three were tightening
   Their harness on their backs,
The Consul was the foremost man
   To take in hand an axe:
And Fathers, mixed with Commons,
   Seized hatchet, bar, and crow,
And smote upon the planks above,   **140**
   And loosed the props below.

Meanwhile the Tuscan army,
   Right glorious to behold,
Came flashing back the noonday light,
Rank behind rank, like surges bright

Of a broad sea of gold.
Four hundred trumpets sounded
    A peal of warlike glee,
As that great host, with measured tread,
And spears advanced, and ensigns spread,   150
Rolled slowly towards the bridge's head,
    Where stood the dauntless Three.

The Three stood calm and silent
    And looked upon the foes,
And a great shout of laughter
    From all the vanguard rose:
And forth three chiefs came spurring
    Before that deep array;
To earth they sprang, their swords they drew,
And lifted high their shields, and flew   160
    To win the narrow way:

Aunus from green Tifernum,
    Lord of the Hill of Vines;
And Seius, whose eight hundred slaves
    Sicken in Ilva's mines;
And Picus, long to Clusium
    Vassal in peace and war,
Who led to fight his Umbrian powers
From that grey crag where, girt with towers,
The fortress of Nequinum lowers   170
    O'er the pale waves of Nar.

Stout Lartius hurled down Aunus
    Into the stream beneath:
Herminius struck at Seius,
    And clove him to the teeth:
At Picus brave Horatius
    Darted one fiery thrust,

185

And the proud Umbrian's gilded arms
   Clashed in the bloody dust.

Then Ocnus of Falerii   180
   Rushed on the Roman Three;
And Lausulus of Urgo,
   The rover of the sea;
And Aruns of Volsinium,
   Who slew the great wild boar,
The great wild boar that had his den
Amidst the reeds of Cosa's fen,
And wasted fields, and slaughtered men,
   Along Albinia's shore.

Herminius smote down Aruns: 190
   Lartius laid Ocnus low:
Right to the heart of Lausulus
   Horatius sent a blow.
"Lie there," he cried, "fell pirate!
   No more, aghast and pale,
From Ostia's walls the crowd shall mark
The track of thy destroying bark;
No more Campania's hinds shall fly
To woods and caverns when they spy
   Thy thrice accursèd sail."   200

But now no sound of laughter
   Was heard among the foes.
A wild and wrathful clamour
   From all the vanguard rose.
Six spears' length from the entrance
   Halted that deep array,
And for a space no man came forth
   To win the narrow way.

But hark! the cry is Astur:
   And lo! the ranks divide;   210

And the great Lord of Luna
   Comes with his stately stride.
Upon his ample shoulders
   Clangs loud the fourfold shield,
And in his hand he shakes the brand
   Which none but he can wield.

He smiled on those bold Romans
   A smile serene and high;
He eyed the flinching Tuscans,
   And scorn was in his eye.   **220**
Quoth he, "The she-wolf's litter
   Stand savagely at bay:
But will ye dare to follow,
   If Astur clears the way?"

Then, whirling up his broadsword
   With both hands to the height,
He rushed against Horatius,
   And smote with all his might.
With shield and blade Horatius
   Right deftly turned the blow.   **230**
The blow, though turned, came yet too nigh;
It missed his helm, but gashed his thigh:
The Tuscans raised a joyful cry
   To see the red blood flow.

He reeled, and on Herminius
   He leaned one breathing-space;
Then, like a wild-cat mad with wounds,
   Sprang right at Astur's face:
Through teeth and skull and helmet
   So fierce a thrust he sped,   **240**
The good sword stood a hand-breadth out
   Behind the Tuscan's head.

And the great Lord of Luna
   Fell at that deadly stroke,
As falls on Mount Alvernus
   A thunder-smitten oak.
Far o'er the crashing forest
   The giant arms lie spread;
And the pale augurs, muttering low,
   Gaze on the blasted head.   **250**

On Astur's throat Horatius
   Right firmly pressed his heel,
And thrice and four times tugged amain
   Ere he wrenched out the steel.
"And see," he cried, "the welcome,
Fair guests, that waits you here!
What noble Lucumo comes next
   To taste our Roman cheer?"

But at his haughty challenge
   A sullen murmur ran,   **260**
Mingled of wrath and shame and dread,
   Along that glittering van.
There lacked not men of prowess,
   Nor men of lordly race;
For all Etruria's noblest
   Were round the fatal place.

But all Etruria's noblest
   Felt their hearts sink to see
On the earth the bloody corpses,
   In the path the dauntless Three: **270**
And, from the ghastly entrance
   Where those bold Romans stood,
All shrank, like boys who, unaware,
Ranging the woods to start a hare,
Come to the mouth of the dark lair

Where, growling low, a fierce old bear
  Lies amidst bones and blood.

Was none who would be foremost
  To lead such dire attack:
But those behind cried "Forward!"   280
  And those before cried "Back!"
And backward now and forward
  Wavers the deep array;
And on the tossing sea of steel
  To and fro the standards reel;
And the victorious trumpet-peal
  Dies fitfully away.

Yet one man for one moment
  Stood out before the crowd;
Well known was he to all the Three,   290
  And they gave him greeting loud,—
"Now welcome, welcome, Sextus!
  Now welcome to thy home!
Why dost thou stay and turn away?
  Here lies the road to Rome!"

Thrice looked he at the city;
  Thrice looked he at the dead;
And thrice came on in fury,
  And thrice turned back in dread:
And, white with fear and hatred,   300
  Scowled at the narrow way,
Where, wallowing in a pool of blood,
  The bravest Tuscans lay.

But meanwhile axe and lever
  Have manfully been plied;
And now the bridge hangs tottering
  Above the boiling tide.

"Come back, come back, Horatius!"
   Loud cried the Fathers all.
"Back, Lartius! back, Herminius!   310
   Back, ere the ruin fall!"

Back darted Spurius Lartius;
   Herminius darted back:
And, as they passed, beneath their feet
   They felt the timbers crack.
But when they turned their faces,
   And on the further shore
Saw brave Horatius stand alone,
   They would have crossed once more.

But with a crash like thunder   320
   Fell every loosened beam,
And, like a dam, the mighty wreck
   Lay right athwart the stream.
And a long shout of triumph
   Rose from the walls of Rome,
As to the highest turret-tops
   Was splashed the yellow foam.

And, like a horse unbroken
   When first he feels the rein,
The furious river struggled hard,   330
   And tossed his tawny mane,
And burst the curb, and bounded,
   Rejoicing to be free,
And, whirling down, in fierce career,
Battlement and plank and pier,
   Rushed headlong to the sea.

Alone stood brave Horatius,
   But constant still in mind;
Thrice thirty thousand foes before,
   And the broad flood behind.   340

"Down with him!" cried false Sextus,
  With a smile on his pale face.
"Now yield thee," cried Lars Porsena,
  "Now yield thee to our grace."

Round turned he, as not deigning
  Those craven ranks to see;
Naught spake he to Lars Porsena,
  To Sextus naught spake he;
But he saw on Palatinus
  The white porch of his home;   350
And he spake to the noble river
  That rolls by the towers of Rome.

"Oh, Tiber! father Tiber!
  To whom the Romans pray,
A Roman's life, a Roman's arms,
  Take thou in charge this day!"
So he spake, and speaking sheathed
  The good sword by his side,
And with his harness on his back
  Plunged headlong in the tide.   360

No sound of joy or sorrow
  Was heard from either bank;
But friends and foes in dumb surprise
With parted lips and straining eyes,
  Stood gazing where he sank;
And when above the surges
  They saw his crest appear,
All Rome sent forth a rapturous cry,
And even the ranks of Tuscany
  Could scarce forbear to cheer.   370

But fiercely ran the current,
  Swollen high by months of rain:

And fast his blood was flowing,
    And he was sore in pain,
And heavy with his armour,
    And spent with changing blows;
And oft they thought him sinking,
    But still again he rose.

Never, I ween, did swimmer,
    In such an evil case,   380
Struggle through such a raging flood
    Safe to the landing place:
But his limbs were borne up bravely
    By the brave heart within,
And our good father Tiber
    Bore bravely up his chin.

"Curse on him!" quoth false Sextus;
    "Will not the villain drown?
But for this stay, ere close of day
    We should have sacked the town!"   390
"Heaven help him!" quoth Lars Porsena,
    "And bring him safe to shore,
For such a gallant feat of arms
    Was never seen before."

And now he feels the bottom;
    Now on dry earth he stands;
Now round him throng the Fathers
    To press his gory hands;
And now, with shouts and clapping,
    And noise of weeping loud,   400
He enters through the River-Gate,
    Borne by the joyous crowd.

They gave him of the corn-land,
    That was of public right,

As much as two strong oxen
   Could plough from morn till night;
And they made a molten image,
   And set it up on high,
And there it stands unto this day
   To witness if I lie.   410

It stands in the Comitium,
   Plain for all folk to see;
Horatius in his harness,
   Halting upon one knee:
And underneath is written,
   In letters all of gold,
How valiantly he kept the bridge
   In the brave days of old.

And still his name sounds stirring
   Unto the men of Rome,   420
As the trumpet-blast that cries to them
   To charge the Volscian home;
And wives still pray to Juno
   For boys with hearts as bold
As his who kept the bridge so well
   In the brave days of old.

And in the nights of winter,
   When the cold north winds blow,
And the long howling of the wolves
   Is heard amidst the snow;   430
When round the lonely cottage
   Roars loud the tempest's din,
And the good logs of Algidus
   Roar louder yet within;

When the oldest cask is opened,
   And the largest lamp is lit;

When the chestnuts glow in the embers,
    And the kid turns on the spit;
When young and old in circle
    Around the firebrands close;   440
When the girls are weaving baskets,
    And the lads are shaping bows;

When the goodman mends his armour,
    And trims his helmet's plume;
When the goodwife's shuttle merrily
    Goes flashing through the loom;
With weeping and with laughter
    Still is the story told,
How well Horatius kept the bridge
    In the brave days of old.   450

LORD MACAULAY

THE ICE FLOES

Dawn from the foretop! Dawn from the barrel!
A scurry of feet with a roar overhead;
The master-watch wildly pointing to northward,
Where the herd in front of *The Eagle* was spread!

Steel-planked and sheathed like a battleship's nose,
She battered her path through the drifting floes;
Past slob and growler we drove, and rammed her
Into the heart of the patch and jammed her.
There were hundreds of thousands of seals, I'd swear,
In the stretch of that field—"white harps" to spare   10
For a dozen such fleets as had left that spring
To share in the general harvesting.
The first of the line, we had struck the main herd;

194

The day was ours, and our pulses stirred
In that brisk, live hour before the sun,
At the thought of the load and the sweepstake won.

We stood on the deck as the morning outrolled
On the fields its tissue of orange and gold,
And lit up the ice to the north in the sharp,
Clear air; each mother-seal and its "harp"   20
Lay side by side; and as far as the range
Of the patch ran out we saw that strange,
And unimaginable thing
That sealers talk of every spring—
The "bobbing-holes" within the floes
That neither wind nor frost could close;
Through every hole a seal could dive,
And search, to keep her brood alive,
A hundred miles it well might be,
For food beneath that frozen sea.   30
Round sunken reef and cape she would rove,
And though the ice and current drove
The ice-fields many leagues that day,
We knew she would turn and find her way
Back to the hole, without the help
Of compass or log, to suckle her whelp—
Back to that hole in the distant floes,
And smash her way up with teeth and nose.
But we flung those thoughts aside when the shout
Of command from the master-watch rang out.   40

Assigned to our places in watches of four—
Over the rails in a wild carouse,
Two from the port and starboard bows,
Two from the broadsides—off we tore,
In the breathless rush for the day's attack,
With the speed of hounds on a caribou's track.
With the rise of the sun we started to kill,

A seal for each blow from the iron bill
Of our gaffs. From the nose to the tail we ripped
    them,
And laid their quivering carcasses flat   50
On the ice; then with our knives we stripped them
For the sake of the pelt and its lining of fat.
With three fathoms of rope we laced them fast,
With their skins to the ice to be easy to drag,
With our shoulders galled we drew them, and cast
Them in thousands around the watch's flag.
Then, with our bodies begrimed with the reek
Of grease and sweat from the toil of the day,
We made for *The Eagle*, two miles away,
At the signal that flew from her mizzen-peak.   60
And through the night, as inch by inch
She reached the pans with the harps piled high,
We hoisted them up as the hours filed by
To the sleepy growl of the donkey-winch.

Over the bulwarks again we were gone,
With the first faint streaks of a misty dawn;
Fast as our arms could swing we slew them,
Ripped them, "sculped" them, roped, and drew them
To the pans where the seals in pyramids rose
Around the flags on the central floes,   70
Till we reckoned we had nine thousand dead
By the time the afternoon had fled;
And that an added thousand or more
Would beat the count of the day before.
So back again to the patch we went
To haul, before the day was spent,
Another load of four "harps" a man,
To make the last the record pan.

And not one of us saw, as we gaffed and skinned
And took them in tow, that the north-east wind   80

Had veered off-shore; that the air was colder;
That the signs of recall were there to the south,
The flag of *The Eagle*, and the long, thin smoulder
That drifted away from her funnel's mouth.
Not one of us thought of the speed of the storm
That hounded our tracks in the day's last chase
(For the slaughter was swift, and the blood was warm),
Till we felt the first sting of the snow in our face.

We looked south-east, where, an hour ago,
Like a smudge on the sky-line, someone had seen   90
The Eagle, and thought he had heard her blow
A note like a warning from her sirene.
We gathered in knots, each man within call
Of his mate, and slipping our ropes, we sped,
Plunging our way through a thickening wall
Of snow that the gale was driving ahead.
We ran with the wind on our shoulder; we knew
That the night had left us this only clue
Of the track before us, though with each wail
That grew to the pang of a shriek from the gale,   100
Some of us swore that *The Eagle* screamed
Right off to the east; to others it seemed
On the southern quarter and near, while the rest
Cried out with every report that rose
From the strain and the rend of the wind on the floes
That *The Eagle* was firing her guns to the west.
And some of them turned to the west, though to go
Was madness—we knew it and roared; but the notes
Of our warning were lost as a fierce gust of snow
Eddied, and strangled the words in our throats.   110
Then we felt in our hearts that the night had swallowed
All signals, the whistle, the flare, and the smoke
To the south; and like sheep in a storm we followed
Each other; like sheep we huddled and broke.

197

Here one would fall as hunger took hold
Of his step; here one would sleep as the cold
Crept into his blood, and another would kneel
Athwart the body of some dead seal,
And with knife and nails would tear it apart,
To flesh his teeth in its frozen heart.   120
And another dreamed that the storm was past,
And raved of his bunk and brandy and food,
And *The Eagle* near, though in that blast
The mother was fully as blind as her brood.
Then we saw what we feared from the first—dark places
Here and there to the left of us, wide, yawning spaces
Of water; the fissures and cracks had increased
Till the outer pans were afloat, and we knew,
As they drifted along in the night to the east,
By the cries we heard, that some of our crew   130
Were borne to the sea on those pans and were lost.
And we turned with the wind in our faces again,
And took the snow with its lancing pain,
Till our eyebrows cracked with the salt and the frost;
Till only iron and fire that night
Survived on the ice as we stumbled on;
As we fell and rose and plunged—till the light
In the south and east disclosed the dawn,
And the sea heaving with floes—and then,
The Eagle in wild pursuit of her men.   140

And the rest is as a story told,
Of a dream that belonged to a dim, mad past,
Of a March night and a north wind's cold,
Of a voyage home with a flag half-mast;
Of twenty thousand seals that were killed
To help to lower the price of bread;
Of the muffled beats . . . of a drum . . . that filled
A nave . . . at our count of sixty dead.

E. J. PRATT

THE CROW AND THE NIGHTHAWK

For any golfer of resource,
The most exhilarating course
I know of has been bedded down
Beside an old Ontario town.
Along the links, the player sees
A motley grove of ancient trees,
While near them, on ungodly ground,
An old distillery is found.
Back in the days when first I knew
The joys of stance and follow-through,   10
That course was crowded with delight
From summer dawn to summer night.
Players were many, but still more
Were all the wild birds, score on score,
Who thronged the grove and thronged the green
And every fairway in between.
Wherever sprinklers wet the ground,
The hungry robins marched around
And, with their black beaks making passes,
Dragged juicy worms from dewy grasses.   20
Yet some there were who said the birds
Were given to unkindly words,
For meadowlarks were far from nice
In jeering at each hook and slice,
And every golfer in the rough
Heard cheeky blackbirds give him guff.

Now two outstanding birds there were
To give the place strong character.
One was a crow, as tough and black
As any fierce demoniac   30

That ever haunted cave or tomb
With accents hoarse and face of doom.
The startled golfers, every one,
Knew him as "Satan", for his fun
Seemed based on murdering the neighbours
Amid their friendly sports and labours.
He seemed to think the raven race
Entitled, for its living space,
To all the world, and thought it good
To slay the feathered brotherhood.   40
And so his kids, the little yeggs,
Were fed on larks' and bluebirds' eggs;
And young song-sparrows, all alive,
He took to make his youngsters thrive.
The master-race of black-plumed devils
Thus loved to murder in their revels.

The other bird of whom I spoke
Was "Hank", the nighthawk, one whose joke
It was with swooping wings to zoom
Above us in the gathering gloom,   50
Intent to see our golf-balls roll
Through twilight to the eighteenth hole.
He was a harmless sort of critter
In handsome uniform of feathers,
Playful in pleasant times and bitter,
And cheerful in all sorts of weathers.
Yet he had thoughts too deep for words,
A loyalty beyond all proof—
It was a nest of baby birds
Upon the old distillery roof.   60

Now, in that summer I recall,
We saw a sort of madness fall
Upon all birds of every sort
In that green-carpeted resort.

The golfers were all heavy smokers
Of every brand of cigarette.
One day the sparrows—always jokers—
Picked up some butts, left burning yet.
The smoke inhaled was good, they found,
And so they passed the word around   70
Till every bird on every green
Was crazy over nicotine.
A butt was scarcely tossed away
Before some feathered scavenger
Had seized the treasure where it lay
And with his little wings a-whir
Flew with it to some branch, to sit
And puff the fag out, bit by bit.
"Satan", of course, performed his share
In this new prank, so tough and rare,   80
Yet he had scorn for little pets
Who only took to cigarettes.
For he would choose, as regulars,
The solid butts of black cigars.
Hank liked the smaller, milder smoke.
But practised, as a kind of joke,
Dive-bombing with his fag, and roaming
With trailing sparks across the gloaming.

"Satan" grew tougher every day,
And once, when Hank was far away,   90
He sought the nighthawk's nest, to kill
The little nestlings, thus to fill
Himself and all his greedy brood
With raw, dismembered flesh for food.
The raid succeeded. Hank came back
Too late to stop the dark attack.
And when, with Mrs. Hank, he went
To call on "Satan" at his nest
In a tall pine-tree, there to vent

201

The anger of a heart distressed,   100
They found the crow, with happy croak,
Having an after-dinner smoke.
Making contemptuous grimaces,
He blew cigar-smoke in their faces.

It was the first day of July
That saw this dirty deed of blood.
Homeward they turned, with many a sigh,
When Hank was startled by the thud
And loud report of firecrackers
From crowds of gay, young bivouackers   110
Who sought with noise to celebrate
The happy birthday of their state.
His bright eyes flashed. He did not loiter,
But cruised about to reconnoitre;
Then hurtled down without a pause
And picked up in his bony claws
A lighted cracker, from whose fuse
The sparks were spitting to amuse
Small boys at play. Up soared the bird
One, two, three hundred feet, and heard   120
The boys and golfers roar surprise
At the strange sight before their eyes.
His ceiling reached, he turned to dive,
With sputtering bomb-load all alive:
Straight at the crow's nest and its crew,
Down, ever faster down, he flew,
And with a bang would fairly scare ye
Hit fairly on the target area,
While he, with skill of wing and eye,
Veered off in safety to the sky.   130
The bursting cracker filled the air
With croaks and corpses and despair.
Down from the pine we saw them go—
Scorched chunks of old and baby crow.

202

A rain of feathers, beaks and legs,
And wreckage of once rifled eggs.
"Satan", too tough to blow apart,
Fell shrieking down, and with a start,
We saw the battered crow expire
Four minutes later, spitting fire.   **140**
Some folk marked him as he fell,
Proclaimed this as a sign of hell;
The truth is that the blitz's jar
Had made him gulp his lit cigar,
And then in anguish writhe and hop
With poisoned flames inside his crop,
Ending a life of utter sin
With fierce heart-burnings deep within.

Then peace returned to bless the earth,
A peace unknown since "Satan's" birth;   **150**
And every nest in bush and tree
Was blest with sweet serenity.
Appalled by "Satan's" end obscene,
The birds abjured all nicotine.
(No nestlings, since that awful death,
Complain about their parents' breath.)
Since then, through all the feathered nation,
The proudest theme of conversation
Is the stout nighthawk's swift reproof;
While on the old distillery roof   **160**
Successive broods of little Hanks
Rise up to give their father thanks.

WATSON KIRKCONNELL

THE BROTHERS

All morning they had quarrelled as they worked,
A little off their fellows, in the pit:
Dick growled at Robert; Robert said Dick shirked;
And when the roof, dropt more than they had reckoned,
Began to crack and split,
Though each rushed like a shot to set
The pit-props in their places.
Each said the other was to blame
When, all secure, with flushed and grimy faces
They faced each other for a second: 10
All morning they had quarrelled, yet
Neither had named her name.

Again they turned to work,
And in the dusty murk
Of that black gallery,
Which ran out three miles underneath the sea,
There was no sound at all
Save whispering creak of roof and wall
And crack of coal and tap of pick,
And now and then a rattling fall,   20
While Robert worked on steadily, but Dick
In fits and starts, with teeth clenched tight
And dark eyes flashing in his lamp's dull light.

And when he paused, nigh spent, to wipe the sweat
From off his dripping brow, and Robert turned
To fling some idle gibe at him, the spark
Of anger smouldering in him flared and burned,
Through all his body quivered, wringing wet.
Till that black hole

204

To him blazed red   30
As if the very coal
Had kindled underfoot and overhead:
Then gripping tight his pick
He rushed upon his brother,
But Robert, turning quick,
Leapt up, and now they faced each other.

They faced each other—Dick with arm upraised
In act to strike, and murder in his eyes . . .
When suddenly with noise of thunder
The earth shook round them, rumbling over and
    under;   40
And Dick saw Robert lying at his feet,
As close behind the gallery crashed in,
And almost at his heel earth gaped asunder.
By black disaster dazed,
His wrath died, and he dropped his pick
And staggered dizzily and terror-sick:
But when the dust and din
Had settled to a stillness dread as death,
And he once more could draw his breath,
He heaved a little joyous shout   50
To find the lamps had not gone out.

And on his knees he fell
Beside his brother buried in black dust,
And, full of tense misgiving,
He lifted him and thrust
A knee beneath his head and cleared
The dust from mouth and nose, but could not tell
Awhile if he were dead or living.
Too fearful to know what he feared,
He fumbled at the open shirt   60
And felt till he could feel the heart

Still beating with a feeble beat,
And then he saw the closed lids part
And saw the nostrils quiver,
And knew his brother lived, though sorely hurt.

Again he staggered to his feet,
And fetched his water-can and wet
The ashy lips and bathed the brow,
Until his brother sat up with a shiver
And gazed before him with a senseless stare   70
And dull eyes strangely set.
Too well Dick knew that now
They must not linger there,
Cut off from all their mates, to be o'ertaken
In less than no time by the deadly damp;
So, picking up his lamp,
He made his brother rise,
Then took him by the arm
And shook him till he'd shaken
An inkling of the danger and alarm   80
Into those dull, still eyes,
Then dragged him and half carried him in haste
To reach the airway where 'twould still be sweet
When all the gallery was foul with gas;
But, soon as they had reached it, they were faced
By a big fall of roof they could not pass,
And found themselves cut off from all retreat
On every hand by that black shining wall,
With naught to do but sit and wait
Till rescue came, if rescue came at all   90
And did not come too late.
And in the fresher airway light came back
To Robert's eyes, although he never spoke,
And not a sound the deathly silence broke
As they sat staring at the wall of black—

206

As in the glimmer of the dusky lamp
They sat and wondered, wondered if the damp—
The stealthy after-damp that, creeping, creeping,
Takes strong lads by the throat and drops them
    sleeping,
To wake no more for any woman's weeping—   100
Would steal upon them ere the rescue came . . .
And if the rescuers would find them sitting,
Would find them squatted on their hunkers, cold . . .
Then as they sat and wondered, like a flame
One thought burned up both hearts—
Still neither breathed her name.

And now their thoughts dropped back into the pit,
And through the league-long galleries went flitting
With speed no fall could hold:
They wondered how their mates had fared—   110
If they'd been struck stone-dead,
Or if they shared
Like fate with them, or reached the shaft
Unhurt and only scared
Before disaster overtook them:
And then, although their courage ne'er forsook them,
They wondered once again if they must sit
Awaiting death . . . but knowing well
That even for a while to dwell
On such-like thoughts will drive a strong man daft, 120
They shook themselves until their thoughts ran free
Along the drift and clambered in the cage,
And in a trice were shooting up the shaft.
But when their thoughts had come to the pithead,
And found the fearful people gathered there
Beneath the noonday sun,
Bright-eyed with terror, blinded by despair,
Dick rose and with his chalk wrote on the wall

This message for his folk:
We can't get any farther—12, noonday— 130
And signed both names; and when he'd done,
Though neither of them spoke,
They both felt easier in a way
Now that they'd left a word,
Though nothing but a scrawl.

And silent still they sat
And never stirred:
And Dick's thoughts dwelt on this and that—
How, far above their heads upon the sea
The sun was shining merrily, 140
And in its golden glancing
The windy waves were dancing;
And how he'd slipped that morning on his way;
And how on Friday when he drew his pay
He'd buy a blanket for his whippet, Nell—
He felt dead certain she would win the race
On Saturday . . . though you could never tell,
There were such odds against her . . . but his face
Lit up as though even now he saw her run—
A little slip of lightning in the sun: 150
While Robert's thoughts were over on the match
His team was booked to play on Saturday—
He placed the field and settled who should play
In Will Burn's stead; for Will he had a doubt
Was scarcely up to form, although . . .

Just then the lamp went slowly out.

Still neither stirred
Nor spoke a word
Though either's breath came quickly, with a catch

And now again one thought   **160**
Set both their hearts afire—
In one fierce flame
Of quick desire,
Though neither breathed her name.

Then Dick stretched out his hand and caught
His brother's arm, and whispered in his ear:
Bob, lad, there's naught to fear . . .
And when we're out, lad, you and she shall wed.
Bob gripped Dick's hand; and then no more was said
As slowly all about them rose   **170**
The deadly after-damp; but close
They sat together hand in hand.
Then their minds wandered—and Dick seemed to stand
And shout till he was hoarse
To speed his winning whippet down the course . . .
And Robert, with the ball
Secure within his oxter, charged ahead
Straight for the goal, and none could hold,
Though many tried a fall.

Then dreaming they were lucky boys in bed   **180**
Once more and lying snugly by each other,
Dick, with his arms clasped tight about his brother,
Whispered with failing breath
Into the ear of death:
Come, Robert, cuddle closer, lad—it's cold.

WILFRID GIBSON

THE MOUNTAIN WHIPPOORWILL*

(How Hill-Billy Jim Won the Great Fiddlers' Prize)

Up in the mountains, it's lonesome all the time,
(Sof' win' slewin' thu' the sweet-potato vine).

Up in the mountains, it's lonesome for a child,
(Whippoorwills a-callin' when the sap runs wild).

Up in the mountains, mountains in the fog,
Everythin's as lazy as an old houn' dog.

Born in the mountains, never raised a pet,
Don't want nuthin' an' never got it yet.

Born in the mountains, lonesome-born,
Raised runnin' ragged thu' the cockleburs and corn.   10

Never knew my pappy, mebbe never should.
Think he was a fiddle made of mountain-laurel wood.

Never had a mammy to teach me pretty-please.
Think she was a whippoorwill a-skitin' thu' the trees.

Never had a brother ner a whole pair of pants,
But when I start to fiddle, why, yuh got to start to dance!

Listen to my fiddle—"Kingdom Come!" "Kingdom Come!"
Hear the frogs a-chunkin' "Jug o' rum, Jug o' rum!"
Hear that mountain whippoorwill be lonesome in the air,
An' I'll tell yuh how I travelled to the Essex County Fair. 20

Essex County has a mighty pretty fair,
All the smarty fiddlers from the South come there.

*Rinehart & Company, Inc., for "The Mountain Whippoorwill" by Stephen Vincent Benét, from *Ballads and Poems, 1915-1930*. Copyright 1931 by Stephen Vincent Benét.

Elbows flyin' as they rosin up the bow
For the First Prize Contest in the Georgia Fiddlers' Show.

Old Dan Wheeling, with his whiskers in his ears,
King-pin fiddler for nearly twenty years.

Big Tom Sargent, with his blue wall-eye,
An' Little Jimmy Weezer that can make a fiddle cry.

All sittin' roun', spittin' high an' struttin' proud,
(Listen, little whippoorwill, yuh better bug yore eyes!)   30
Tun-a-tun-a-tunin' while the jedges told the crowd
Them that got the mostest claps 'd win the bestest prize.

Everybody waitin' for the first tweedle-dee,
When in comes a'stumblin'—hill-billy me!

Bowed right pretty to the jedges an' the rest,
Took a silver dollar from a hole inside my vest,

Plunked it on the table an' said, "There's my callin' card!
An' anyone that licks me—well, he's got to fiddle hard!"

Old Dan Wheeling, he was laughin' fit to holler,
Little Jimmy Weezer said, "There's one dead dollar!"   40

Big Tom Sargent had a yaller-toothy grin,
But I tucked my little whippoorwill right underneath my
    chin,
An' petted it an' tuned it till the jedges said, "Begin!"

Big Tom Sargent was the first in line;
He could fiddle all the bugs off a sweet-potato vine.

He could fiddle down a possum from a mile-high tree,
He could fiddle up a whale from the bottom of the sea.

211

Yuh could hear hands spankin' till they spanked each other
   raw,
When he finished variations on "Turkey in the Straw".

Little Jimmy Weezer was the next to play;   50
He could fiddle all night, he could fiddle all day.

He could fiddle chills, he could fiddle fever,
He could make a fiddle rustle like a lowland river.

He could make a fiddle croon like a lovin' woman,
And they clapped like thunder when he'd finished strummin'.

Then came the ruck of the bobtailed fiddlers,
The let's-go-easies, the fair-to-middlers.

They got their claps, an' they lost their bicker,
An' they all settled back for some more corn-licker.

An' the crowd was tired of their no-count squealing,   60
When out in the centre steps Old Dan Wheeling.

He fiddled high and he fiddled low,
(Listen, little whippoorwill, yuh got to spread yore wings!)
He fiddled and fiddled with a cherrywood bow.
(Old Dan Wheeling's got bee-honey in his strings.)

He fiddled the wind by the lonesome moon,
He fiddled a most almighty tune.

He started fiddling like a ghost,
He ended fiddling like a host.

He fiddled north and he fiddled south,   70
He fiddled the heart right out of yore mouth.

He fiddled here and he fiddled there,
He fiddled salvation everywhere.

When he was finished, the crowd cut loose,
(Whippoorwill, they's rain on yore breast.)
And I sat there wonderin', "What's the use?"
(Whippoorwill, fly home to yore nest.)

But I stood up pert, an' I took my bow,
An' my fiddle went to my shoulder, so.

An'—they wasn't no crowd to get me fazed—   80
But I was alone where I was raised.

Up in the mountains, so still it makes yuh skeered,
Where God lies sleepin' in his big white beard.

An' I heard the sound of the squirrel in the pine,
An' I heard the earth a-breathin' thu' the long night-time.

They've fiddled the rose an' they've fiddled the thorn,
But they haven't fiddled the mountain-corn.

They've fiddled sinful an' fiddled moral,
But they haven't fiddled the breshwood-laurel.

They've fiddled loud, an' they've fiddled still,   90
But they haven't fiddled the whippoorwill.

I started off with a dump-diddle dump,
(Oh, hell's broke loose in Georgia!)
Skunk-cabbage growin' by the bee-gum stump.
(Whippoorwill, yo're singin' now!)

Oh, Georgia booze is mighty fine booze,
The best yuh ever poured yuh,
But it eats the soles right offen yore shoes,
For hell's broke loose in Georgia.

My mother was a whippoorwill pert,   100
My father, he was lazy,

213

But I'm hell broke loose in a new store shirt
To fiddle all Georgia crazy.

Swing yore partners—up and down the middle!
Sashay now—oh, listen to that fiddle!
Flapjacks flippin' on a red-hot griddle,
An' hell broke loose,
Hell broke loose,
Fire on the mountains—snakes in the grass.
Satan's here a-bilin'—oh, Lordy, let him pass!   110
Go down Moses, set my people free;
Pop goes the weasel thu' the old Red Sea!
Jonah sittin' on a hickory-bough,
Up jumps a whale—an' where's yore prophet now?
Rabbit in the pea-patch, possum in the pot,
Try an' stop my fiddle, now my fiddle's gettin' hot!
Whippoorwill, singin' thu' the mountain hush,
Whippoorwill, shoutin' from the burnin' bush,
Whippoorwill, cryin' in the stable-door,
Sing tonight as yuh never sang before!   120
Hell's broke loose like a stompin' mountain-shoat,
Sing till yuh bust the gold in yore throat!
Hell's broke loose for forty miles aroun',
Bound to stop yore music if yuh don't sing it down.
Sing on the mountains, little whippoorwill,
Sing to the valleys, an' slap 'em with a hill,
For I'm struttin' high as an eagle's quill,
An' hell's broke loose,
Hell's broke loose,
Hell's broke loose in Georgia!   130

They wasn't a sound when I stopped bowin',
(Whippoorwill, yuh can sing no more.)
But, somewhere or other, the dawn was growin',
(Oh, mountain whippoorwill!)

214

An' I thought, "I've fiddled all night an' lost.
Yo're a good hill-billy, but yuh've been bossed."

So I went to congratulate old man Dan,
—But he put his fiddle into my han' —
An' then the noise of the crowd began!

STEPHEN VINCENT BENÉT

IF

If you can keep your head when all about you
    Are losing theirs and blaming it on you;
If you can trust yourself when all men doubt you,
    But make allowance for their doubting too;
If you can wait and not be tired by waiting,
    Or being lied about, don't deal in lies,
Or being hated don't give way to hating,
    And yet don't look too good, nor talk too wise.

If you can dream—and not make dreams your master;
    If you can think—and not make thoughts your aim; 10
If you can meet with Triumph and Disaster
    And treat those two impostors just the same;
If you can bear to hear the truth you've spoken
    Twisted by knaves to make a trap for fools,
Or watch the things you gave your life to broken,
    And stoop and build 'em up with worn-out tools.

If you can make one heap of all your winnings
    And risk it on one turn of pitch-and-toss,
And lose, and start again at your beginnings
    And never breathe a word about your loss;   **20**

215

If you can force your heart and nerve and sinew
    To serve your turn long after they are gone,
And so hold on when there is nothing in you
    Except the Will which says to them: "Hold on!"

If you can talk with crowds and keep your virtue,
    Or walk with Kings—nor lose the common touch,
If neither foes nor loving friends can hurt you,
    If all men count with you, but none too much;
If you can fill the unforgiving minute
    With sixty seconds' worth of distance run,   30
Yours is the Earth and everything that's in it,
    And—which is more—you'll be a Man, my son!

Rudyard Kipling

LONDON UNDER BOMBARDMENT

I, who am known as London, have faced stern times before,
Having fought and ruled and traded for a thousand years
    and more;
I knew the Roman legions and the harsh-voiced Danish
    hordes;
I heard the Saxon revels, saw blood on the Norman swords.
But, though I am scarred by battle, my grim defenders vow
Never was I so stately nor so well-beloved as now.
The lights that burn and glitter in the exile's lonely dream,
The lights of Piccadilly, and those that used to gleam
Down Regent Street and Kingsway may now no longer shine,
But other lights keep burning, and their splendour, too, is
    mine,   10
Seen in the work-worn faces and glimpsed in the steadfast
    eyes

When little homes lie broken and death descends from the
    skies.
The bombs have shattered my churches, have torn my streets
    apart,
But they have not bent my spirit and they shall not break
    my heart.
For my people's faith and courage are lights of London town
Which still would shine in legends though my last broad
    bridge were down.

GRETA BRIGGS

VESTIGIA

I took a day to search for God,
And found Him not. But as I trod
By rocky ledge, through woods untamed,
Just where one scarlet lily flamed,
I saw His footprint in the sod.

Then suddenly, all unaware,
Far off in the deep shadows, where
A solitary hermit thrush
Sang through the holy twilight hush—
I heard His voice upon the air.   10

And even as I marvelled how
God gives us Heaven here and now,
In a stir of wind that hardly shook
The poplar leaves beside the brook—
His hand was light upon my brow.

At last with evening as I turned
Homeward, and thought what I had learned

217

And all that there was still to probe—
I caught the glory of His robe
Where the last fires of sunset burned.   **20**

Back to the world with quickening start
I looked and longed for any part
In making saving Beauty be . . .
And from that kindling ecstasy
I knew God dwelt within my heart.

BLISS CARMAN

THIS WAS MY BROTHER

This was my brother
At Dieppe,
Quietly a hero
Who gave his life
Like a gift,
Withholding nothing.

His youth . . . his love . . .
His enjoyment of being alive . . .
His future, like a book
With half the pages still uncut—   **10**

This was my brother . . .
At Dieppe . . .
The one who built me a doll house
When I was seven,
Complete to the last small picture frame,
Nothing forgotten.

218

He was awfully good at fixing things,
At stepping into the breach when he was needed.

That's what he did at Dieppe;
He was needed.   20
And even Death must have been a little shamed
By his eagerness!

MONA GOULD

CARGOES

Quinquereme of Nineveh from distant Ophir,
Rowing home to haven in sunny Palestine,
With a cargo of ivory,
And apes and peacocks,
Sandalwood, cedarwood, and sweet white wine.

Stately Spanish galleon coming from the Isthmus,
Dipping through the Tropics by the palm-green shores,
With a cargo of diamonds,
Emeralds, amethysts,
Topazes, and cinnamon, and gold moidores.   10

Dirty British coaster with a salt-caked smoke-stack,
Butting through the Channel in the mad March days,
With a cargo of Tyne coal,
Road-rails, pig-lead,
Firewood, iron-ware, and cheap tin trays.

JOHN MASEFIELD

MACAVITY: THE MYSTERY CAT

Macavity's a Mystery Cat: he's called the Hidden Paw—
For he's the master criminal who can defy the Law.
He's the bafflement of Scotland Yard, the Flying Squad's
    despair:
For when they reach the scene of crime—*Macavity's not
    there!*

Macavity, Macavity, there's no one like Macavity,
He's broken every human law, he breaks the law of gravity.
His powers of levitation would make a fakir stare,
And when you reach the scene of crime—*Macavity's not
    there!*
You may seek him in the basement, you may look up in the
    air—
But I tell you once and once again, *Macavity's not there!* 10

Macavity's a ginger cat, he's very tall and thin;
You would know him if you saw him, for his eyes are
    sunken in.
His brow is deeply lined with thought, his head is highly
    domed;
His coat is dusty from neglect, his whiskers are uncombed.
He sways his head from side to side, with movements like
    a snake;
And when you think he's half asleep, he's always wide awake.

Macavity, Macavity, there's no one like Macavity,
For he's a fiend in feline shape, a monster of depravity.
You may meet him in a by-street, you may see him in the
    square—
But when a crime's discovered, then *Macavity's not there!* 20

He's outwardly respectable. (They say he cheats at cards.)
And his footprints are not found in any file of Scotland
    Yard's.
And when the larder's looted, or the jewel-case is rifled,
Or when the milk is missing, or another Peke's been stifled,
Or the greenhouse glass is broken, and the trellis past re-
    pair—
Ay, there's the wonder of the thing! *Macavity's not there!*

And when the Foreign Office find a Treaty's gone astray,
Or the Admiralty lose some plans and drawings by the way,
There may be a scrap of paper in the hall or on the stair—
But it's useless to investigate—*Macavity's not there!*   30
And when the loss has been disclosed, the Secret Service say:
"It *must* have been Macavity!"—but he's a mile away.
You'll be sure to find him resting, or a-licking of his thumbs,
Or engaged in doing complicated long division sums.

Macavity, Macavity, there's no one like Macavity,
There never was a Cat of such deceitfulness and suavity.
He always has an alibi, and one or two to spare:
At whatever time the deed took place—MACAVITY WASN'T
    THERE!
And they say that all the Cats whose wicked deeds are widely
    known
(I might mention Mungojerrie, I might mention Griddle-
    bone)   40
Are nothing more than agents for the Cat who all the time
Just controls their operations: the Napoleon of Crime!

T. S. ELIOT

OLD SUSAN

When Susan's work was done, she'd sit
With one fat guttering candle lit,
And window opened wide to win
The sweet night air to enter in.
There, with a thumb to keep her place,
She'd read, with stern and wrinkled face,
Her mild eyes gliding very slow
Across the letters to and fro,
While wagged the guttering candle flame
In the wind that through the window came.   10
And sometimes in the silence she
Would mumble a sentence audibly,
Or shake her head as if to say,
"You silly souls, to act this way!"
And never a sound from night I'd hear,
Unless some far-off cock crowed clear;
Or her old shuffling thumb should turn
Another page; and rapt and stern,
Through her great glasses bent on me,
She'd glance into reality;   20
And shake her round old silvery head,
With—"You!—I thought you was in bed!"
Only to tilt her book again,
And rooted in romance remain.

WALTER DE LA MARE

222

THE OLD MILL

These once-proud walls are utterly undone;
   And yet, in mute remembrance of the past,
They lift their wounded columns to the sun
   And lean in broken grandeur on the blast.

The winds have brought them healing which atones
   For all their wounds; and 'neath attendant skies
Old moons will wine the chalice of their stones
   And golden noons will stain them with warm dyes.

I hear this gentle stream, that gave us bread,
   Sing sweetly on the Old Mill's echoing stone,   **10**
Lest we forget those Words that once were said
   That mankind shall not live by bread alone.

The wheels are silent now, and yet is milled
   Pale grist that once was warm as autumn's gold;
And on clear nights transparent sacks are filled
   By cloudy shapes that move as men of old.

And misty farmers ride up with their grain;
   And spectral horses neigh against the door;
And streams of blurring amber pour in vain
   Their flood of ghostly wheat forevermore.   **20**

And all these phantom millers move in rhyme
   Even as when in life; and on clear nights
You can behold them toiling as though time
   Had never passed the Humber's silvered heights.

WILSON MACDONALD

NIGHT-DRIVING

Night-driving: When the trees like cardboard scenery rush
    towards one
And pass: but more crane forward and take their place.
Strange to follow two great rays of light; yet one pursues
    them always.
Now a stone wall bordering; now a hedge—deep ditches—
    pitfalls of a foggy night
But in the clear moonlight, only trimmings to the road.
Suddenly a village—hushed and sleeping and one wonders
    for a moment
Of the lives of those who live therein—Humble? Contented?
    Ambitious? Who knows?
But the windows give back nothing. Blank, expressionless
    like blind eyes or a mask.
And so the open country once again. Each indentation of
    the surface
Exaggerated: each bump a hill, each dip a valley.   10
Now a white signpost with pointing digits offering alter-
    natives—
Four routes to choose from—each perhaps as charming, so
    how decide?
But symbolic of life: our way is set, and one way only leads
    us to our destination.
And so we rush on, seemingly the only live thing in this
    great world of darkness.
Tangible earth below us and vast mystery of sky above.

ARTHUR EMERSON McFARLANE

THE FRUIT-RANCHER

He sees the rosy apples cling like flowers to the bough;
He plucks the purple plums and spills the cherries on the
grass;
He wanted peace and silence,—God gives him plenty now—
His feet upon the mountain and his shadow on the pass.

He built himself a cabin from red cedars of his own;
He blasted out the stumps and twitched the boulders from
the soil;
And with the axe and chisel he fashioned out a throne
Where he might dine in grandeur off the first-fruits of his
toil.

His orchard is a treasure-house alive with song and sun,
Where currants ripe as rubies gleam and golden pippins
glow;   10
His servants are the wind and rain whose work is never done
Till winter rends the scarlet roof and banks the halls with
snow.

He shouts across the valley and the ranges answer back;
His brushwood smoke at evening lifts a column to the moon;
And dim beyond the distance where the Kootenai snakes
black,
He hears the silence shattered by the laughter of the loon.

                                          LLOYD ROBERTS

THE PALATINE

"Have you been with the king to Rome,
Brother, big brother?"
"I've been there and I've come home.
Back to your play, little brother."

"Oh, how high is Caesar's house,
Brother, big brother?"
"Goats about the doorways browse;
Nighthawks nest in the burnt roof-tree.
Home of the wild bird and home of the bee,
A thousand chambers of marble lie   10
Wide to the sun and wind and the sky.
Poppies we find amongst our wheat
Grow on Caesar's banquet seat.
Cattle crop and neatherds drowse
On the floors of Caesar's house."

"But what has become of Caesar's gold,
Brother, big brother?"
"The times are bad and the world is old—
Who knows the where of the Caesar's gold?
Night comes black o'er the Caesar's hill;   20
The wells are deep and the tales are ill;
Fireflies gleam in the damp and mould—
All that is left of the Caesar's gold.
Back to your play, little brother."

"What has become of the Caesar's men,
Brother, big brother?"

"Dogs in the kennel and wolf in the den
Howl for the fate of the Caesar's men,
Slain in Asia, slain in Gaul,
By Dacian border and Persian wall.   30
Rhineland orchard and Danube fen
Fatten their roots on Caesar's men."

"Why is the world so sad and wide,
Brother, big brother?"
"Saxon boys by their fields that bide
Need not know if the world is wide.
Climb no mountain but Shere-end Hill,
Cross no water but goes to mill.
Ox in the stable and cow in the byre,
Smell of the wood smoke and sleep by the fire;   40
Sunup in seedtime—a likely lad
Hurts not his head that the world is sad.
Back to your play, little brother."

                                        WILLA CATHER

NOTATION ON IMMORTALITY

We sat debating many things together,
Old Rover drowsy on the floor, and then,
Watching him hunt in dreams, we argued whether
A dog will live again.

Searching the scriptures, "Perish as a beast"
We could recall, and in another place,
"Without are dogs"—in all the scroll no least
Promise for Rover's race.

Lean and unkempt beside his owner's chair
He sprawled. We could not clearly picture him   **10**
Ranging around with sheep burrs in his hair,
Among the seraphim.

The fire went out; the hall clock struck eleven.
Stretching, he sighed, and edged a little way
Nearer his master's foot—already in heaven
And asking but to stay.

NANCY BYRD TURNER

VITAI LAMPADA

There's a breathless hush in the Close tonight—
  Ten to make and the match to win—
A bumping pitch and a blinding light,
  An hour to play and the last man in.
And it's not for the sake of a ribboned coat,
  Or the selfish hope of a season's fame,
But his Captain's hand on his shoulder smote—
  "Play up! play up! and play the game!"

The sand of the desert is sodden red,—
  Red with the wreck of a square that broke;—   **10**
The Gatling's jammed and the Colonel dead,
  And the regiment blind with dust and smoke.
The river of death has brimmed his banks,
  And England's far, and Honour a name,
But the voice of a schoolboy rallies the ranks:
  "Play up! play up! and play the game!"

This is the word that, year by year,
    While in her place the School is set,
Every one of her sons must hear,
    And none that hears it dare forget.   20
This they all with a joyful mind
    Bear through life like a torch in flame,
And falling fling to the host behind—
    "Play up! play up! and play the game!"

SIR HENRY NEWBOLT

NOTES

PART ONE

DUNKIRK

3   Written in 1941. The evacuation of the British forces from Dunkirk was one of the most dramatic events of World War II. It was made necessary when, in May, 1940, the German armies broke through the Allied lines, confining more than 400,000 British and French troops in an ever-diminishing pocket along the French coast. More than a thousand craft, most of them manned by civilian volunteers, took part in the rescue of the trapped forces. In all, 336,000 Allied soldiers were transported from Dunkirk across the Straits of Dover to the safety of the English shore. The evacuation began on May 29 and was completed on June 4.   8 **leech**: edge.
24 **Flanders**: the most westerly province of Belgium, bordering on the North Sea.   35 **a penoncel**: a narrow pointed streamer, attached to the head of a lance. It was awarded to a young knight as a mark of special distinction.   42 **racing *M***: a special class of fast, powerful racing yacht fifty-five feet in length.   67 **came about**: changed direction while still heading into the wind.   86 **the *Victory***: the British flagship at the battle of Trafalgar.   87 **sullen twist**: The right side of Nelson's face was somewhat drawn as the result of a wound suffered in his early years of service.   88 **were out**: were in readiness for firing.   88 ***The Golden Hind***: Drake's ship.   97 **stays**: ropes supporting the mast.   97 **conned**: directed how to steer.   101 **held him true**: kept him on course.

LOCHINVAR

6   This ballad is taken from Scott's *Marmion*, 1808. It is based on an old folk ballad, "Katherine Jaffray", which dealt with an actual happening in early Scottish history. Lochinvar was a chief of the Gordon clan in Dumfriesshire in south-western Scotland. Netherby Hall was in Cumberland, England, a short distance across the Border.   7 **brake**: thicket.   8 **Eske river**: a small river in Dumfriesshire, near the Border.   20 **Solway**: a deep firth on the west coast of Britain between England and Scotland. It is noted for its high tides.   22 **measure**: dance.   32 **galliard**: a kind of lively dance.   39 **croupe**: the position on a horse's back behind the saddle.   41 **scaur**: bare hillside.

231

THE SQUAD OF ONE

8   Written in 1917.   This ballad is based on a story told to the poet when he was a boy, by a corporal of the Royal North-West Mounted Police. Names and places have been changed, as have some of the original facts.   3 **Snake Creek Bend**: represented as being in southern Alberta near the United States border.   26 **jumper sleigh:** a simple kind of log sleigh practical for use in rough country.   30 **Okotoks:** a town in southern Alberta, about a hundred miles north of the United States border.   40 **horn:** drink.   40 **jumper:** see note on line 26 above.   40 **grip:** valise.   60 **the "Riders of the Plains"**: a popular name for the Royal North-West Mounted Police (since 1920, the Royal Canadian Mounted Police).

BISHOP HATTO

12   This ballad is based on a legend of the tenth century. Hatto was the Archbishop of Mentz in western Germany. The island and castle to which he is represented as having fled for safety are in the middle Rhine, a short distance below the town of Bingen.   In the original legend he was said to have been devoured by an army of mice.   63 **told:** counted.

THE "LAUGHING SALLY"

15   The incident related in this ballad is fictitious.   1 **Pernambuco:** The most easterly state of Brazil, forming a large cape jutting out into the Atlantic.   7 **The black flag:** the flag of piracy. It was a white skull and cross-bones on a black background.   11 **black:** threatening danger.   11 **let slip:** released in pursuit of prey.   27 **liana'd:** covered with climbing plants. A liana is any kind of vine.   28 **bayou:** sluggish swampy body of water, here the sheltered mouth of the river.   51 **bides:** waits.

CASEY AT THE BAT

18   This poem first appeared in the San Francisco *Examiner* in 1888.

JACQUES CARTIER

20   Written in 1858. This poem deals with the second voyage of Cartier to the New World. The expedition, consisting of three ships and 120 men, set out from St. Malo on May 16, 1536, and returned on July 16, 1537. Cartier was a native of St. Malo, as were most of his crew. The town is in Brittany, near the west end

232

of the north coast of France. 21 **Thulé**: the name given by the
ancients to the northernmost part of the habitable world. 25
strain: mood. 29 **clad**: clothed. 40 **crown**: a shield bearing the arms of France. Actually Cartier erected the cross and
crown not at Hochelaga (Montreal) but at Stadacona (Quebec).

BETH GELERT

22 This ballad is based on a Welsh legend of the early thirteenth
century. Llewelyn, Prince of Wales, known as Llewelyn the Great,
was the last of the native rulers of his country. Gelert was a valuable greyhound that had been given to him by King John of England.
The tomb, or what is said to be the tomb, of Gelert may still be
seen in the valley of Beddgelert in the Snowdonia area of North
Wales. Enclosed by an iron paling and standing in a small meadow,
it is a famous Welsh landmark. Beth is the English spelling of the
Welsh word "bedd" which means "grave". Hence the title may be
translated "The Grave of Gelert". 3 **brach**: female hound.
22 **chidings**: loud baying of hounds. 23 **Snowdon**: a mountain
in north-western Wales. 30 **portal-seat**: castle door. 44
blood-gouts: spots of blood. 46 **covert**: bedcover. 48 **be-
sprent**: splashed. 69 **scath**: injury. 83 **marbles storied**:
marble tablets bearing an account of the incident.

SIR SMASHAM UPPE

26 Written in 1933. 17 **Queen Anne**: Furniture of the
Queen Anne period—early eighteenth century—is rare and costly.

THE LITTLE BOATS OF BRITAIN

27 Written in 1941. See the note on "Dunkirk", page 231. 6
King Leopold: the King of Belgium, whose unexpected surrender of
his country to the Germans on May 28, 1940, made imperative the
immediate withdrawal of the British forces.

HOW THEY BROUGHT THE GOOD NEWS

29 The ride described in this poem has no historical foundation.
Browning meant it to be understood as occurring during the struggle
of the Netherlands for independence from Spain at the beginning
of the seventeenth century. He explained that the three riders were
supposed to be carrying from Ghent to Aix, by "some unsuspected
line of road", news that relief was on its way to the besieged city.
The route they are represented as following may be traced on a

map of Belgium. It runs from west to east, the distance being about 125 miles. Ghent is in west central Belgium and Aix-la-Chapelle is in western Germany near the Belgian border. The poet wrote the poem on the fly-leaf of a book which he happened to have in his hand while sitting in a deck-chair on board a ship bound for Italy. 3 **watch:** warder of the gate. 10 **pique:** raised part of the saddle in front of the rider. 17 **half-chime:** bells chiming the half-hour. 28 **askance:** sideways, i.e., questioningly. 49 **buffcoat:** heavy padded leather jacket. 50 **jack-boots:** heavy boots, reaching above the knees and designed to protect the legs.

THE PRIEST AND THE MULBERRY TREE

31   The mulberry is a small tree that grows in temperate climates. It bears sweet berry-like fruit, dark purple or blackish in colour, which hangs in clusters. 13 **to boot:** as well.

BONNIE GEORGE CAMPBELL

32   The story told in this old ballad is based on an actual happening that took place in Scotland in very early times. There are a number of different versions of the poem. 2 **Tay:** a river in Perthshire in central Scotland. The Campbell clan is widely settled throughout this part of the country. 10 **greetin' fu' sair:** weeping very bitterly. 12 **rivin':** tearing. 14 **corn is unshorn:** grain is not harvested. 21 **toom:** empty.

THE CREMATION OF SAM McGEE

33   Published in 1907. At the time, Service was employed as a bank clerk at White Horse in the Yukon Territory. 1 **in the midnight sun:** in the arctic region, where during the summer season the sun is above the horizon twenty-four hours a day. 2 **the men who moil for gold:** In 1898 "free" or placer gold was discovered in the Yukon territory of Canada. Within a year more than thirty thousand men from all over the world had hastened into the gold fields. 2 **moil:** work laboriously, often in mire or wet. 7 **marge:** margin, shore. 13 **mushing our way:** making our way on snowshoes behind the dog sleds. 13 **the Dawson trail:** Dawson City was the centre of the mining area. 35 **huskies:** Eskimo dogs.

THE GLOVE AND THE LIONS

37   The incident related in this poem took place at the court of Francis I, King of France, 1515-47. One of the favourite amuse-

ments of the king and his nobles was to watch combats among the lions which were kept in a menagerie on the Rue des Lions near the palace. 7 **ramped**: reared on their hind legs with their forepaws in the air.

KING JOHN AND THE ABBOT OF CANTERBURY

38   This old ballad was composed originally in the fifteenth century, but the version that has come down to us is a modernized one of a considerably later date. Although the story may have a basis of fact, it is for the most part fictitious. Tales of this nature involving questions and answers were popular in mediaeval times. 4 **he did great wrong**: King John, 1167-1216, is said to have been the worst king and the cruellest man ever to occupy the throne of England.   8 **rode post**: rode quickly, with changes of horses at regular intervals along the road.   11 **gold chains**: stewards. A steward wore a gold chain as a badge of his office.   20 **gear**: wealth.   42 **Oxenford**: Oxford.   64 **your quarrel**: the complaint against you.   71 **crozier**: abbot's staff, carried as a symbol of his office.   71 **mitre**: abbot's head-dress.   71 **rochet**: abbot's close-sleeved linen robe.   71 **cope**: abbot's long flowing outer cloak, worn on ceremonial occasions.   81 **thirty pence**: Judas received thirty pieces of silver for betraying Christ. See Matthew, Chapter XXVI, verses 47 to 50 and Chapter XXVII, verses 3 to 5.   85 **St. Bittle**: probably St. Botolph. "Bittle" is used for purposes of rhyme.   93 **St. Jone**: probably St. John.   105 **noble**: an old English gold coin worth about five dollars.

JOHNNY APPLESEED

42   Johnny Appleseed, whose real name was Jonathan Chapman, was a strange backwoods wanderer, who, between 1801 and 1847, tramped thousands of miles through Ohio and Indiana, planting apple seeds wherever he went. At this time, the apple tree, which originally had been introduced into the American colonies from England, was not grown west of the Alleghenies; and Appleseed, who was obsessed with the urge to spread its cultivation to the western settlements, would collect the seeds each autumn from cider-presses in western Pennsylvania and then plant them the next spring and summer in suitable locations in Ohio and Indiana. On later journeys he would either transplant the young trees or give them to the local settlers. During his forty-six years of travelling, he traversed more than a hundred thousand square miles of territory. He died in the summer of 1847 at the home of a backwoodsman to

whose cabin he had walked twenty miles the previous day. The details of his life as given in the poem are true to fact. **58 in the sear:** worn with age. He was seventy-two when he died. **73 winding sheet:** sheet in which the body of a dead person is wrapped.

THE WALRUS AND THE CARPENTER

45 This poem is found in *Through the Looking Glass*, 1871, in which it is recited to Alice by Tweedledee. **80 Turning a little blue:** Blue-point oysters are much used for eating raw.

THE ADMIRAL'S GHOST

49 17 Nelson: Lord Nelson, 1758-1805, was the most famous English admiral of the time of the Napoleonic Wars. He and Sir Francis Drake are considered to have been England's two greatest naval leaders. **19 patch . . . sleeve:** Nelson lost his right eye and his right arm in his earlier years of service. **21 Devonshire:** a county in south-western England on the English Channel. Drake was a Devonshire man. **24 Hardy:** Nelson's flag-captain at Trafalgar. He was standing beside Nelson on the deck of the *Victory* when the admiral received his death wound. **36 cocked hat:** a hat with large stiff flaps turned up to a peaked crown. It is part of the uniform of a British naval officer. **43 astarn:** astern, i.e., back in time. **47 Drake:** Sir Francis Drake, 1545-96, was an English admiral. He became famous for his raids on Spanish settlements in the New World and for his being the first English commander to circumnavigate the globe. He particularly distinguished himself as vice-admiral of the English fleet in the engagement with the Spanish Armada, 1588. He died on shipboard during an expedition against the Spaniards and was buried at sea. **48 Nombre Dios Bay:** a small bay on the north-east coast of Panama. **52 Plymouth Sound:** an important seaport in Devonshire. It was Drake's home and the starting-point of his various expeditions. **59 box your compass right:** check your bearings. **74 round shot:** cannon ball. **92 Trafalgar's Bay:** a small bay on the south-west coast of Spain. At the battle of Trafalgar, October 21, 1805, Nelson defeated the combined French and Spanish fleets, destroying or capturing two-thirds of their ships. This engagement, which ended the danger of an invasion of England by Napoleon, is regarded as being the most brilliant victory in Britain's naval history.

THE WHITE SHIP

53 The events related in this ballad took place on the night of November 25-26, 1120. The details are as described in the poem.

The White Ship sailed for Southampton from Barfleur in Normandy. As a result of careless seamanship, she struck a charted reef not far beyond the harbour mouth and sank in a matter of minutes. Prince William was King Henry's only son. It was not until three days after word of the disaster reached England that anyone dared tell the king. On receiving the news, he fell unconscious from his chair and is said never to have smiled again.   2 **Berold**: the only survivor of the wreck. When the ship sank, he succeeded in seizing hold of the top of the mast, to which he clung, just above water, until rescued in the morning.   7 **King Henry**: Henry I, King of England, 1100-35. He was the third of the Norman kings of England, being the youngest son of William the Conqueror.   28 **the White Ship**: The White Ship was a swift Norman galley. Her captain had requested and been granted by the king the privilege of carrying to England the prince and the other members of the royal party.   39 **beck**: bidding, command.   61 **Fitz-Stephen**: the captain of the White Ship, who had been entrusted by the king with the safety of the prince. His father had commanded the vessel that carried William the Conqueror to England.   64 **pilot**: i.e., captain. 67 **moil**: turmoil.   76 **churn**: churning, agitation.   77 **gulf**: sea.   85 **anear**: near by.   92 **travail**: distress.   107 **maugre**: in spite of.

THE PIED PIPER OF HAMELIN

57   Browning wrote this poem for a young friend, Willie Macready, who was confined to bed by illness. It was written to amuse the boy and to give him material for illustrative drawings. The story is based on a German legend of the fourteenth century.   1 **Hamelin**: a town in north-western Germany about thirty miles from the city of Hanover. It is in the province of Hanover—not in Brunswick.   13 **vats**: wooden tubs.   24 **Corporation**: town council.   37 **guilder**: a gold coin worth about forty cents.   65 **admire**: wonder at.   68 **Trump of Doom**: the trumpet blast on the Day of Judgment.   69 **painted tombstone**: Tombstones in mediaeval times were sometimes gilded.   79 **Pied**: so called because he wore garments of different colours.   87 **old-fangled**: old-fashioned.   89 **Tartary**: a region in Central Asia.   89 **Cham**: Tartar ruler.   91 **Nizam**: native ruler of Hyderabad in India.   125 **he**: i.e., Julius Caesar.   125 **manuscript**: his *Commentary* on his conquest of Gaul.   131 **boards**: covers. 132 **conserve**: preserve, fruit.   133 **train-oil**: whale oil.   138 **drysaltery**: storehouse for dried or salted meats.   139 **nuncheon**: between-meal snack.   141 **puncheon**: large cask.   142 **staved**: broken open.   158 **Claret, Moselle, Vin-de-Grave, Hock**: choice

French and German wines.   160 **Rhenish**: a choice German wine.   177 **Bagdat**: the capital of Iraq in Asia Minor.   179 **Caliph**: Mohammedan ruler.   182 **stiver**: Dutch coin worth about two cents.   258 **heaven's gate opes to the rich . . .** : See Matthew, Chapter XIX, verses 23 and 24.   290 **Transylvania**: a province in north-western Roumania.

THE "REVENGE"

67   The sea fight which is described in this ballad took place on September 10-11, 1591. England and Spain were at war, and ships of the two countries fought one another wherever they met. 1 **Azores**: a group of islands in the North Atlantic, about a thousand miles west of Portugal. Flores is the westernmost island of the group. Here an English squadron was waiting to intercept the homeward-bound treasure-fleet of Spain.   1 **Sir Richard Grenville**: captain of the *Revenge* and second in command of the English squadron.   3 **Spanish ships of war**: the Spanish fleet on its way from Spain to meet the treasure-fleet and escort it home.   4 **Lord Thomas Howard**: the commander of the English squadron. He had been the admiral commanding the English fleet which defeated the Spanish Armada in 1588.   5 **out of gear**: not in fighting trim.   7 **ships of the line**: warships, as distinguished from smaller fighting vessels.   12 **Inquisition dogs**: The Spanish Inquisition was an agency of the Roman Catholic Church in Spain, established to suppress heresy. Its agents frequently tortured English prisoners in an attempt to make them renounce their Protestant faith.   12 **devildoms**: evil practices.   17 **Bideford in Devon**: Sir Richard Grenville's home town from which he had recruited his crew.   24 **huge sea-castles**: Spanish galleons of this period were much higher than were English ships. They usually had either three or four decks.   24 **weather bow**: the side of the bow towards the wind. 30 **Seville**: a port in the south of Spain. Until 1563 it was the capital of that country.   33 **the little *Revenge***: The *Revenge* was of five hundred tons which was average size for English warships of the time. It had been commanded by Drake against the Armada in 1588. However, it appeared small in comparison with the huge Spanish galleons.   50 **the great *San Philip***: The *San Philip* was sunk by the *Revenge*.   57 **the fight of the one and the fifty-three**: In the course of the fifteen-hour fight, the *Revenge* was engaged by fifteen different ships carrying five thousand sailors and soldiers. Of the Spanish ships, five were destroyed with the loss of about eighteen hundred men.   112 **the lands they had ruined**: Spanish America.   114 **or ever**: before.   114 **a**

238

great gale blew: The storm destroyed twenty-nine of the Spanish fleet as well as seventy or more of the treasure-fleet that had just arrived from the Americas. The *Revenge*, with a Spanish crew of two hundred, went down near the island of St. Michael, one of the Azores.

FLANNAN ISLE

72   Flannan Isle is one of a group of small islands on the fringe of the Outer Hebrides off the north-west coast of Scotland. The events related in the poem are based upon an actual incident. 26 **guillemot or shag**: species of large sea-birds.   28 **half-tide**: submerged at full tide.   45 **limewash**: a coating of lime applied to the walls of a lighthouse.

THE TRAPPER AND THE BEARS

75   This poem is taken from *The Flying Bull and Other Tales*, 1940, which is a series of longer narrative poems arranged according to an unusual plan. The story opens in the little Manitoba town of Manitou where a number of people are sitting round the fire in the parlour of the hotel. Eleven of them are passengers of a bus that has been caught in a blizzard and six are local residents. To while away "the dull, interminable day" each person present tells a "tall yarn", beginning with the drover who relates the story of "The Flying Bull". "The Trapper and the Bears", which is the fourth story in the book, is told by the local merchant.   3 **drummer**: commercial traveller.   7 **expostulation**: protest.   21 **Kapuskasing**: a town in Northern Ontario, about 220 miles north of Sault Ste. Marie. 28 **huskies**: Eskimo dogs.   30 **Porquis Junction**: about ninety miles south-east of Kapuskasing.   30 **Hearst**: about sixty miles west of Kapuskasing.   43 **trekked**: travelled slowly and with difficulty.   52 **droves**: masses.   72 **mush**: make one's way on snowshoes behind a dog sled.   88 **pickerel**: a species of the pike family. It reaches a length of about two feet and is an appetizing food fish.   119 **Cree**: member of this particular Algonquin tribe of Indians.   175 **friskers**: playful creatures, such as rabbits and foxes.   181 **Gulliver**: the principal character in Swift's *Gulliver's Travels*, who, in the course of his voyages, visited several strange countries.

PAUL REVERE'S RIDE

82   Paul Revere's midnight ride from Boston to Lexington, on April 18-19, 1775, is one of the most celebrated incidents of Ameri-

can history. A Boston silversmith by trade, Revere, before the night of his history-making ride, had already taken a prominent part in anti-British activities, having been one of the leaders of the "Boston Tea Party" and later a secret agent for the Massachusetts Assembly. The purpose of his ride was to warn the people of the Middlesex countryside north-west of Boston that British troops were on their way to seize the store of patriot arms that had been collected at Concord. Longfellow's account differs from historical fact in two main particulars. First, Revere's friend hung the lanterns in the North Church tower actually as a signal to patriots in Charlestown to inform them of the British plan and to warn them to have a horse ready for Revere. The latter then was rowed across the Charles River from Boston to Charlestown. Secondly, Revere did not reach Concord. He was stopped by a British patrol three miles outside the town. Later he was released without his horse; but meanwhile a rider from Lexington, who had succeeded in escaping the patrol, was able to warn the townspeople.   4 **Hardly a man is now alive**: This ballad was written in 1861. The speaker may be regarded as being an old man who is telling the story to his grandchildren.   7 **by land or sea**: The British had a choice of two routes in marching from Boston to Concord. The southern one was by land all the way, while the northern one (which they took) involved crossing the Charles to the north shore and then following the Medford road.   9 **North Church tower**: prominently situated on a hill in north Boston opposite Charlestown. The tower was blown down by a hurricane in 1954 but was rebuilt with money raised by national subscription. The steeple rises 175 feet in the air.   16 **Charlestown shore**: The village of Charlestown was opposite Boston on the north bank of the Charles.   83 **Mystic**: a small river flowing into the Atlantic near Charlestown. 88 **Medford**: By road, Medford was eight miles north-west of Boston. Lexington was five miles farther on, and Concord was six miles beyond Lexington.   100 **the bloody work**: In the skirmish fought at Lexington the next morning, eight of the patriots were killed and ten wounded. This was the first bloodshed in the American Revolutionary War.   112 **the British fled**: At Concord bridge, the British troops were met and repulsed by the patriot forces which had gathered from the surrounding countryside. As the British soldiers marched the nineteen miles back to Boston, they were continually harassed by the sniping attacks of the angered colonists, losing 273 men, killed, wounded or captured, before reaching the city.   120 **cry of alarm**: "The British are coming!"

THE DEATH OF THE HIRED MAN
87   Written in 1914. The setting of this poem is the New England countryside.   65 **daft**: foolish.

SAM'S THREE WISHES
93   5 **I knows on**: I know of. Sam is supposed to be an English rustic who uses a rural dialect.   7 **nobbut inside 'un**: nobody inside it.   25 **rush**: candle with a wick made from the spongy pith of a rush.   38 **pixy**: fairy.   38 **burn**: glow.   38 **hawthorn**: a flowering shrub or tree with fragrant blossoms, long thorns and small red fruits called haws. The haws (pixy-pears) were supposed to be sacred to the fairies.   40 **fairy-knowes**: fairy-rings. These are circular rings on the grass of a meadow, caused by mushroom growth. In folklore they were supposed to be made by the fairies as they danced in a circle during the night.   42 **Potencies**: beings possessing supernatural powers.   45 **rilling**: tinkling. 50 **crany**: cranium, head.   52 **Michaelmas Day**: September 29th. In certain parts of England it is the custom to have a goose on this day.   61 **flagstones**: flat stones used in surfacing.   75 **stounded**: astounded, struck dumb with wonder.   85 **be turning**: is turning brown, i.e., is cooked.   92 **nowt**: naught, nothing. 112 **dumpity**: short and thick.   118 **shock**: bushy, shaggy. 120 **clodhopping**: heavy and clumsy.   124 **sooth**: soft, smooth. 133 **glour**: glower, stare.   137 **bumpity**: thumping.   139 **giblets**: edible internal parts of a fowl, such as the heart and liver. 170 **Pinks . . . eglantine**: English summer flowers noted for their fragrance.   174 **may**: hawthorn.   195 **gooming**: staring absent-mindedly.   200 **Blue in the air**: In superstition, the burning of a candle with a blue flame is supposed to indicate the presence of unseen spirits.   206 **rattle**: a plant with showy purplish-yellow flowers. When ripe, its seeds rattle in their cases.   218 **Christian**: human.   227 **stave**: sing.   228 **page primus**: the first page.   230 **ad infinitum**: forever.

I'LL FIND A WAY OR MAKE IT
100   2 **Rome's imperial day**: the period of Rome's greatest power. This was in the first and second centuries A.D.   18 **no royal road**: an allusion to the answer of the mathematician Euclid of the fourth century B.C. to Ptolemy, King of Egypt. When the king asked him if geometry could not be made easier, Euclid replied, "There is no royal road to geometry."   22 **Helicon**: a mountain in ancient Greece on whose slopes was a fountain the waters of which were believed to inspire those who drank of them.

OLD IRONSIDES

102   "Old Ironsides" was the name given to the American frigate *Constitution* because of the many successful actions in which she engaged in the thirty years that followed her launching in 1797. These included the capture of various French privateers, the bombardment of the forts at Tripoli, the dictating of peace to the Barbary States, and the sinking and capturing of a number of British ships in the War of 1812. Condemned to be broken up in 1830, "Old Ironsides" was saved by this poem, the publication of which aroused such popular indignation that the ship was rebuilt and placed in dock at Navy Yard, Boston, where she may still be seen, afloat and with sails furled. The vessel is 204 feet in length, with a displacement of 2,250 tons.   15 **harpies**: persons who are greedy and ravenous, in this case the dealers who would profit from the purchase and scrapping of the ship.

LITTLE BATEESE

103   Published in 1901. Drummond is remembered principally for his French-Canadian dialect poems.   2 **gran'père**: grandfather. 19 **toute suite**: at once.   28 **Louis Cyr**: presumably fictitious. 29 **voyageurs**: men employed by the fur companies in transporting goods by land and water to and from the remote trading-posts.

SEA-FEVER

104   Taken from *Salt-Water Ballads*, 1902. Masefield, who was only twenty-four when he wrote this poem, was remembering the sailor's life he had given up to become a writer in London. He had run away to sea when he was fourteen.   3 **wheel's kick**: jerk of the wheel against the helmsman.   12 **trick**: literally, a sailor's turn at the helm, usually of two hours' duration; figuratively, life itself.

CALLED UP

107   This poem appeared in *The Times* of London in 1914 shortly after the outbreak of World War I. Sir Francis Drake, 1545-96, and Lord Nelson, 1758-1805, are regarded as having been England's two greatest naval leaders.   9 **great lights**: searchlights.   10 **thin wires**: telephone and telegraph wires.   11 **three leagues**: nine miles. At the time of Elizabeth I, the maximum range in naval gunnery was less than a thousand yards.   16 **Trafalgar signal**: Nelson's famous message to the fleet at the beginning of the battle of Trafalgar—"England expects every man to do

his duty"—was signalled by flags.   16 **the beating of my drum**: In keeping with Drake's death-bed instructions, the drum that had been used aboard his flagship was placed on the wall of the ancestral Drake home in Devonshire, where it still hangs. According to tradition, the dying commander said, "If England ever is in danger, sound the alarum drum, and I will come."

THE MONKEY

108   A familiar sight in many larger cities, especially in southern Europe and the United States, is the organ-grinder, with his hand organ and his trained monkey. The monkey traditionally is dressed in a scarlet tunic and fez, and begs for coins which are dropped into either his outstretched fez or a cup.   1 **hunched**: crouched. 19 **antic**: clown.

IN FLANDERS FIELDS

109   This poem was written in May, 1915, while McCrae was serving as a surgeon with the Canadian Forces on the Western Front, and was published anonymously in *Punch* on December 8 of that year. It won immediate popularity and is recognized as one of the greatest poems to emerge from World War I.   1 **Flanders**: the most westerly province of Belgium, bordering on the North Sea. In World War I, this part of the Western Front was held by British and Empire troops.   11 **we throw the torch**: In early Scottish times a torch was tossed from the hands of one runner to the next as a message was carried summoning the clans to prepare for battle.

THE DONKEY

109   7 **parody**: ridiculous imitation.   10 **crooked will**: stubbornness.   13 **my hour**: the occasion when Jesus, amid the acclaim of the crowd, entered Jerusalem riding upon a donkey. See John, Chapter XII, verses 12 to 15.

LINCOLN

110   In 1816, when Abraham Lincoln was seven, his family moved to a backwoods farm in southern Indiana. Here the future President of the United States spent his boyhood years. The family was poor even by the standards of that pioneer community.

PART TWO

BANNERMAN OF THE DANDENONG

115   The incident related in this ballad is represented as taking place in the State of Victoria, in south-eastern Australia.   1   **Bush**: an extensive tract of land, covered by stunted forest growth. The term is a common one in Australia.   4   **the Dandenong**: a district in southern Victoria lying immediately west of the city of Melbourne.   7   **the Murray streams in the West**: The Murray, running a course of about 1,200 miles, is the longest river in Australia. Flowing west and then south, it empties into the sea approximately 250 miles west of the Dandenong. The main stream has many tributaries.   21   **fire-floods**: flame streaming through the grass and underbrush.   38   **blue gums**: Australian eucalyptus trees, from which oozes a resinous gum, bluish in colour.   51   **Nammoora**: presumably the name of a ranch—in Australia, called a station.

FIDELE'S GRASSY TOMB

117   1   **The Squire**: the chief landlord of an English county parish.   8   **Orchardleigh**: represented as being in Somersetshire, in south-western England.   13   **a hound of the Danish breed**: a Great Dane.   16   **Elsinore**: a seaport in Denmark. Because of the narrowness of the strait on which the port is situated, the tides there are unusually strong.   18   **"Fidele"**: "Faithful".   20   **chantry**: chapel.   25   **Bath and Wells**: cathedral towns in Somersetshire, in south-western England.   27   **screed**: long letter of complaint.   34   **wax**: readily yielding.   42   **give him a start**: allow him a head start.   55   **Prelate and Prince**: Archbishop.

SIMON LEGREE

120   Much of Lindsay's poetry has a strong appeal to the ear and was written to be read aloud.   **Simon Legree**: a slave trader and brutal villain in Mrs. Harriet Beecher Stowe's novel, *Uncle Tom's Cabin*, 1853.   3   **opulent**: fat.   24   **Uncle Tom**: a Negro slave in the above-mentioned novel, noted for his faithfulness and piety. He was bought by Legree from his first owner and, after passing through the hands of various masters, belonged to Legree again at the time of his death.   26   **Eva**: a kind and beautiful child, the daughter of Tom's first owner. Tom was devoted to her and was deeply saddened by her death, which occurred in the early part of the story.   27   **sanctoriums**: holy places.

244

HEATHER ALE

122   This ballad is based upon an ancient legend of the Galloway district in south-western Scotland.   1 **bonny bells**: beautiful bell-shaped flowers.   2 **long-syne**: long ago.   6 **a blessed swound**: a blissful swoon.   8 **dwellings underground**: caves.   9 **a king in Scotland**: According to tradition, Kenneth MacAlpin, generally described as the first King of Scotland, conquered the Picts about the middle of the ninth century.   10 **fell**: cruel.   11 **Picts**: an ancient race of people, probably Celtic, who, in early times, inhabited parts of the Scottish Highlands.   12 **roes**: deer.   15 **dwarfish**: In legend, the Picts are represented as having been a pygmy race.   23 **Brewsters**: Brewers.   33 **fortuned**: chanced.   34 **free**: carefree.   46 **giddy**: causing dizziness because of its height.   61 **small**: thin.   66 **naught**: nothing.   83 **sapling**: of youth, untried.

THE FORSAKEN

125   Written in 1902.   The poem is based on a story related to the poet when he was travelling in the Great Slave Lake area of the North-West Territories as an agent of the Department of Indian Affairs.   4 **the Fort**: the trading-post of the area.   6 **Chippewa**: a tribe of Indians found scattered throughout the North-West Territories.   21 **lacings**: laces, fastenings.   22 **tikanagan**: a kind of fur-lined sleeping-bag for Indian children.   27 **round**: humped shape.   51 **huskies**: Eskimo dogs.   63 **slunk**: slipped away furtively.   66 **old and useless**: Among some of the Indian tribes, it was the practice of the band at the approach of cold weather to forsake its members who, because of age, could be of no practical use during the ensuing winter season.   72 **in state**: with solemn dignity.   76 **spangled**: sparkling with stars.

ETIQUETTE

128   Taken from *Bab Ballads*, 1869.   Several of the Gilbert and Sullivan operettas grew out of these ballads.   1 **Cariboo**: a fictitious name.   7 **tasted**: tested the quality by tasting.   11 **Alexander Selkirk**: a Scottish sailor, who, in 1704, after an argument with his captain, was marooned on the island of Juan Fernandez in the Pacific Ocean, about 360 miles west of Chile.   He spent four years alone on this island until rescued by a passing vessel.   His experience is believed to have inspired Defoe's *Robinson Crusoe*.   13 **in trade**: in business and consequently of inferior social standing.   33 *mus ridiculus*: literally, tiny mouse, used here in the sense of a creature that is difficult to find, namely, the turtle.   38 **chum-**

245

mies: chums: 38   **Charterhouse**: a famous British boys' public school in Surrey in southern England.   40   **hummed and hawed**: made inarticulate sounds, indicative of doubt about the wisdom of his action.   64   **the City**: the principal business district of London, England.   70   **a convict ship**: a vessel employed in transporting convicts to a penal colony.   70   **Portland**: a small peninsula on the English Channel, where convicts were held, waiting transportation to a penal colony.   74   **pulling stroke**: pulling the oar on the port (left) side, nearest the stern, in which position he would be setting the stroke for the other rowers.   79   **tack**: course.   84   **cut each other dead**: ignored each other completely.

"KILMENY"

132   Published in 1919.   During World War I, England was blockaded tightly by German submarines.   When a small craft such as a fishing-trawler or a slow merchantman was intercepted, the submarine, in order to save torpedoes, would surface and attack with its deck guns.   The British countered these tactics by placing camouflaged guns on apparently unarmed ships.   *Kilmeny* is represented as being one of these.   Often when a submarine on the surface approached its intended victim, a fierce duel for survival took place. 1   **drifters**: fishing-vessels, used in time of war for laying anti-submarine devices.   2   **long meshes of steel**: anti-submarine nets, sometimes several miles in length.   6   **tapping unseen**: The ship was receiving orders on her wireless by a secret naval code.   8 **nobody knew**: The captain would have had sealed orders directing him to a particular location at sea, where the presence of an enemy submarine was suspected.   9   **Newcastle**: a city in north-eastern England, noted for its iron foundries.   10   **the Clyde**: a river in western Scotland, along which are located a number of world-famous ship-yards.   14   **The laughter of London**: the contemptuous laughter of the British people at the boasting of the German government. 14   **the boasts of Berlin**: The German government publicly boasted that the submarine blockade would "bring England to her knees, begging for peace".   20   **"Well done"**: In the Royal Navy, this is a traditional signal from the admiral in praise of a successful action performed by a ship under his command.   21   **a conger**: a kind of large deep-sea eel.   25   **a wandering shadow**: the grief-stricken widow of the skipper.

THE SLAVE'S DREAM

133   Written in 1842.   It was one of a number of poems written by Longfellow in support of the anti-slavery cause.   8   **Niger**: a river of West Africa.   28   **tamarind**: a tropical tree cultivated

for its leaves, flowers and fruit.   29 **Caffre**: a Negro race inhabiting the south-eastern corner of Africa. Its people, who were
noted for their fine physique and warlike nature, were highly prized
by the slave traders. *Kafir* is a more common spelling.   33
river-horse: hippopotamus.

A BALLAD OF JOHN SILVER

135   Taken from *Salt-Water Ballads*, 1902. John Silver was the
leader of the pirate crew in Stevenson's *Treasure Island*.   1
schooner-rigged: with fore-and-aft sails, enabling the vessel to tack
more closely into the wind.   1 **rakish**: having the masts sloping.
3 **Jolly Roger**: the pirate flag. It was a white skull and cross-bones
on a black background.   4 **the Spanish Water**: the water off
the eastern coast of Spanish America, especially the north coast of
South America from the Isthmus of Panama to the mouth of the
Amazon.   8 **We laid their ships aboard**: We placed our ship
close alongside theirs for the purpose of attacking and boarding.
9 **chains**: fastenings for the ropes that support the masts.   21
quidding: chewing tobacco.   22 **Board of Trade**: a committee
established by the British government, and responsible, in the eighteenth century, for matters relating to trade and foreign plantations.
One of its principal tasks was the suppression of piracy.   24
Islands of the Blest: in ancient mythology a group of islands somewhere in the West, where the favourites of the gods were taken at
death to dwell in everlasting happiness.

DANIEL WEBSTER'S HORSES

136   Daniel Webster, 1782-1852, was one of the greatest of
American statesmen and orators. He spent much of his time at his
country estate near Marshfield, Massachusetts, where he took great
pride in his fine horses and where, according to local legend, the
incident occurred which provides the background for this poem.

ON THE WAY TO THE MISSION

137   Written in 1905. The incident related in this poem is
represented as taking place in the Province of Quebec in the area
lying north of the lower St. Lawrence River.   15 **wood-pigeon**:
a kind of large wild dove.   28 **silver fox-skin**: one of the most
prized of furs.   29 **pelts of mink and of otter**: furs of great
value.   47 **Montagnais**: a tribe of Indians inhabiting the area
between the lower St. Lawrence River and the Laurentian height of
land.   53 **bloodroot . . . windflower**: delicate white wild flowers
of the early spring.

247

THE QUAKER'S MEETING

139   The incident related in this poem is represented as taking place in England in the eighteenth century. The Quakers were members of the Society of Friends, a religious denomination founded by George Fox about 1650, and dedicated to peace, plainness of dress, simple traditional speech ("yea", "nay", "thee", "thou"), and frequent attendance at religious meetings.   1   **wilds**: lonely heath. 3 **His hat it was broad**: The hats worn by Quakers in these early times had unusually wide brims.   7   **merry blink**: encouraging glance.   25   **lead**: pistol bullet.   34   **Mammon**: the greed of wealth. In the New Testament, Mammon was the demon of cupidity. 41   **Jimmy Barlow**: fictitious.   42   **Friend—**: This was a customary form of greeting among Quakers.   49   **popped**: shot.   52 **brace**: pair.   56   **riddle**: a kind of coarse sieve.   57   **diddled**: tricked.   57   **game**: courageous.   59   **scrapers**: heels.

THE TWA CORBIES

142   This old ballad, which is of Scottish origin, dates from very early times. Although it is possible that the poem may be based on an actual happening, no proof of this has been discovered.   2 **twa corbies**: two ravens. The raven is a glossy black bird very much like the crow but somewhat larger.   2   **mane**: moan, lament. 3   **tane**: one.   5   **yon auld fail dyke**: yonder old turf wall. 6   **wot**: know.   7   **kens**: knows.   13   **hause-bane**: neck-bone. 14   **pike**: pick.   14   **eyne**: eyes.   15   **ae**: one.   15   **gowden**: golden.   16   **theek**: thatch.

THE SHOOTING OF DAN McGREW

143   This poem was published in 1907. The setting is represented as being in Dawson City, Yukon Territory, during the time of the gold rush of 1898. According to the poet's own statement, the story is wholly fictitious.   1   **Malamute**: Eskimo dog.   2 **music-box**: piano.   2   **jag-time tune**: gay and noisy tune.   3 **solo game**: game of solitaire.   4   **light-o'-love**: sweetheart.   6 **the creeks**: the streams in the valley of the Yukon along which gold was mined.   6   **loaded for bear**: looking for trouble.   8   **tilted**: partially emptied.   8   **poke of dust**: pouch of gold dust.   14 **green stuff**: whiskey poured from a green bottle.   17   **rubbering**: moving in curiosity.   19   **rag-time**: a kind of music characterized by vigorous rhythm.   21   **buckskin**: a strong soft leather, usually yellowish or greyish.   23   **Great Alone**: arctic wilderness.   40 **spread misere**: In some games of solitaire, this declaration is made by the player as an acknowledgment that he has lost his game. 56   **hooch**: raw liquor.   58   **pinched**: slyly stole.

CHRISTMAS AT SEA

146   4 **a-lee**: in the direction towards which the wind is blowing. 8 **to go about**: to tack, to change direction while still heading into the wind.   9 **South Head**: A head, or headland, is a point of land stretching out into the sea.   13 **tide-race**: the ebbing or flowing of the tide with great force into a narrow channel.   18 **long-shore**: on shore.   19 **volleyed out**: sent out the smoke in puffs.   33 **high sea light**: elevated light on shore to guide ships into the harbour.   37 **bearings**: true course.   38 **smelt**: searched carefully.   42 **nose**: front end, prow.   42 **handsome**: proudly.

ROBIN HOOD AND ALAN A DALE

149   This old ballad was composed in the fourteenth century. It is one of a number that describe the exploits of Robin Hood, a legendary English outlaw who lived with his band of merry companions in Sherwood Forest, Nottinghamshire. As the years passed, his fair-dealing, generosity and sense of humour established him as a popular English hero. Nothing is actually known about him except what is told in the ballads themselves.   4 **Nottinghamshire**: in north-eastern England.   6 **the greenwood tree**: representative of the woodlands in summer, especially as the scene of outlaw life.   44 **Alan a Dale**: Alan of the Dale.   51 **a book**: possibly, though not necessarily, a copy of the Bible.   58 **stint nor lin**: loiter nor stop.   63 **I am a bold harper**: Wandering minstrels were always welcomed warmly in mediaeval times.   71 **finikin**: dainty.   72 **glistering**: glistening.   91 **three times asked in the church**: English law requires the declaration of intention to marry (publishing of the banns) at three different church services. 96 **The cloth doth make thee a man**: Clerical attire enables you to perform the offices of a clergyman.   97 **choir**: used here to indicate the front part of the church, in which services are conducted.   98 **The people began for to laugh**: As Little John was the biggest of Robin Hood's band, the Bishop's coat, worn over his outlaw garb, would not fit him properly.

PAUL BUNYAN

153   Paul Bunyan was a legendary giant lumber-jack of Canada and the northern United States, who was the hero of innumerable stories told in the lumber camps. He piled up the Rocky Mountains, dug the Mississippi River, and logged off the forests where now is prairie. Wherever he walked he left lakes behind in his footsteps. His constant companion was his blue ox, Babe, who could pull the

logs of an entire forest and drink rivers dry. A possible interpretation of this poem might be the representing of the coming and passing of a thunderstorm.   15 **mackinaw coat**: a short, heavy, double-breasted plaid coat, much worn by woodsmen.   16 **logger**: lumber-jack.

THE CALF PATH

155   11 **bell-wether sheep**: the leader of a flock of sheep with a bell on its neck.

THE HIGHWAYMAN

157   In England, during the eighteenth century, stage-coaches were frequently held up by highwaymen. When the operations of one of these law-breakers became notorious in a certain district, squads of red-coats, or regular soldiers, were assigned to capture him.   6 **highwayman**: a man who robs travellers on a main road.   7 **a French cocked-hat**: a hat with stiff flaps turned up so as to form a triangular crown.   18 **love-knot**: a bright ribbon worn in the hair to signify affection.   19 **stable-wicket**: stable door.   20 **peaked**: sickly.   38 **tawny**: yellow, amber.   39 **gipsy's ribbon**: a brightly-coloured strip of silk.   49 **to attention**: in rigid military position.   73 **priming**: powder charge in a musket. This had to be "looked to" or examined when a sure shot was required.

THE "JERVIS BAY" GOES DOWN

161   Written in 1940. This poem records one of the most famous sea fights of World War II. The *Jervis Bay* was an old merchantman that had been reconditioned by the British Navy and equipped as an armed escort vessel. On November 5, 1940, during her first assignment, the convoy which she was accompanying from Canada to England was attacked by a German battleship, the *Admiral Scheer*. The *Jervis Bay* immediately engaged the enemy, drawing upon herself all the fire power of the battleship, and after fifty minutes of fighting was sunk. Meanwhile, most of the ships of the convoy, which had dispersed in the gathering darkness, succeeded in escaping. Sixty-eight members of the crew of the *Jervis Bay* were rescued by a Swedish freighter, which courageously remained near the scene of action until after nightfall. The details of the engagement are based on accounts given by these survivors. For this deed of valour, Captain Feegan of the *Jervis Bay* was post-humously awarded the Victoria Cross.   4 **Singapore**: a British colony in the Straits Settlements at the southern end of the Malay

Peninsula.   6 **the China Seas**: the waters lying off the southern part of the east coast of Asia.   7 **Tasman**: a sea bordering the southern part of the east coast of Australia.   8 **Borneo**: one oɪ the principal islands of the East Indies, lying east of Singapore. 14 **less than fourteen knots**: fifteen or sixteen miles an hour.   24 **field**: basic colour of a flag.   25 **Britain's Naval Reserve**: a force of both active and retired officers of the merchant marine, appointed by the British Admiralty and subject to call to naval duty when required.   27 **frowsed**: untidy.   43 **barrow**: wheelbarrow. 43 **slips**: cuttings from plants, used for transplanting.   47 **breakwater**: a wall-like structure for protecting a harbour from the force of the waves.   54 **reservists**: forces withheld temporarily from action so as to be available for service when needed.   69 **bottoms**: ships.   72 **Up from tropical waters . . . to the Americas**: a voyage of about ten thousand miles.   76 **a harbour of the North**: Halifax, Nova Scotia.   82 **samson posts**: stout posts built into the hold of a merchant vessel to aid in loading and unloading cargo.   83 **chains and blocks**: cranes, used for loading and un-loading cargo.   94 **convoy line**: line of merchant vessels under the protection and charge of a ship of war.   105 **seminars**: theo-logical students.   106 **parka**: long warm jacket with an attached hood.   117 **The ship's bell sounds**: eight o'clock in the morning. 120 **shoots**: checks his position by.   122 **Eight bells again**: four o'clock in the afternoon.   126 **crow's nest**: a partly enclosed platform high on a mast for the look-out man.   132 **hull down**: with its hull below the horizon.   133 **battleship**: The *Admiral Scheer* was a battleship of 10,000 tons, with a speed of 26 knots. She carried 6 11-inch guns with an extreme range of 30,000 yards and 8 5.9-inch guns with a considerably greater range than the 8 5-inch guns of the *Jervis Bay*.   136 **telegraphs**: signals by a bell system of communication.   140 **Goliath**: giant, tremendous. See I Samuel, Chapter XVII, verses 4 to 7.   146 **Krupp plate**: plate armour made in the Krupp steel works in Essen, Germany. It was noted for its extreme hardness.   156 **Nelson**: the admiral com-manding the British fleet at the battle of Trafalgar, 1805.   156 **Drake**: the most famous of the English admirals in attacks against the Spanish at the time of Elizabeth I.   156 **Beatty**: the com-mander of the British cruiser squadron at the battle of Jutland, 1916, and later Admiral of the Fleet.   156 **Harwood**: the commander of the British squadron that crippled the *Graf Spee* (sister ship of the *Admiral Scheer*), December, 1939.   158 **Porter, Farragut**: famous Northern naval commanders at the time of the American Civil War, 1861-5.   158 **John Paul Jones**: the first naval hero of the United States, who distinguished himself on several occasions in actions against superior British naval forces during the American Revolutionary War, 1775-83.   173 **setters**: layers, who plot the bearing of the gun in the vertical plane.   174 **pointers**: trainers, who plot the bearing of the gun in the horizontal plane.   177 **with the top roll of the battleship**: when the battleship is momentarily on an even keel on the crest of a wave.   179 **with the blue field**: Since the *Jervis Bay* was at this time actively engaged in escort duty under the British Naval Reserve, she would be flying a white ensign. 189 **bends**: ties.

THE DEACON'S MASTERPIECE

168   The story told in this poem is represented as taking place in New England.   1 **Shay**: colloquial for chaise, a light two-wheeled one-horse carriage.   10 *Georgius Secundus*: George II, King of England, 1727-60. He was of the German House of Hanover, and was thoroughly German in character and habits.   12 **Lisbon**: the great Lisbon earthquake of November 1, 1755, destroyed most of the city with a loss of about 35,000 lives.   14 **Braddock's army**: In 1755, during the Seven Years' War, a British and Colonial army under General Braddock was ambushed and massacred by the French and their Indian allies near Fort Duquesne (Pittsburgh). 14 **done so brown**: defeated so badly.   20 **felloe**: rim.   20 **thill**: shaft.   21 **panel**: body.   21 **cross-bar**: wooden bar placed beneath the body as a brace.   21 **sill**: main timbers along the base of the body.   22 **thorough-brace**: one of a pair of heavy leather straps under the body, serving as a support.   28 **vum**: vow, swear.   41 **lancewood**: a tough pliable wood, native to the West Indies.   43 **white-wood**: white pine.   45 **"Settler's Ellum"**: elm trees that were standing when the first settlers came.   48 **lips**: saw cuts.   50 **prop-iron**: iron support of the step.   51 **linch-pin**: pin passed through the end of the axle to keep the wheel on.   54 **boot**: cover or apron, attached to the dashboard to protect the passengers from rain and mud.   54 **dasher**: dashboard—a panel attached to the front of the body to keep mud off the passengers.   78 **runs at large**: can be generally applied.   90 **whipple-tree**: pivoting bar to which the horse's traces are fastened.   92 *encore*: again, also.   99 **rat-tailed**: having a long, tapering tail.   99 **ewe-necked**: having a thin, poorly shaped neck.   99 **bay**: horse of a reddish-brown colour.

THE LIGHTHOUSE

172   3 **Head**: A head, or headland, is a point of land stretching out into the sea.   9 **horn**: fog-horn.   110 **belt**: life-belt. 133 *what cheer?*: How are you getting along?   160 **plucked up heart**: regained spirit.

HORATIUS AT THE BRIDGE

180   This ballad is one of the *Lays of Ancient Rome*, 1842. In the poem, a Roman bard of about 390 B.C. is supposed to be giving an account of a happening that took place during the early history of the City, about 510 B.C. There is very little historic foundation for the legend of Horatius and the defence of the bridge.   1 **Lars**: a title of honour meaning the same as chieftain.   1 **Porsena**: the king of Clusium who undertook an expedition against Rome to restore Tarquin to the throne.   1 **Clusium**: the most important of the twelve cities of the Etruscan confederation. It was about ninety miles north of Rome.   2 **the Nine Gods**: the nine great gods of Etruscan mythology.   3 **Tarquin**: the seventh and last of the legendary kings of Rome. Because of his tyranny and cruelty, the Roman people had expelled him and his entire family from the City and had set up the republic.   14 **Etruscan**: The Etruscans inhabited a large territory stretching several hundred miles northward from Rome. Their twelve principal cities were banded together in the Etruscan confederation under Lars Porsena.   25 **Apennine**: The Apennine range of mountains extends down the central part of northern Italy.   30 **Sutrium**: one of the southernmost of the Etruscan cities, about thirty miles north of Rome.   34 **yellow Tiber**: The Tiber is frequently described as yellow because of the volcanic sediment which is carried by its waters, especially in time of flood. Ancient Rome was on the south-east bank of the river.   36 **champaign**: open countryside.   42 **Tarpeian**: a steep rock, eighty feet high, forming part of the Capitoline Hill in Rome.   46 **Fathers**: Senators. They were usually older men.   50 **wis**: suppose.   54 **Consul**: one of the two chief magistrates who headed the government of the City after the expulsion of Tarquin.   64 **Janiculum**: a fortified ridge of land directly across the river from Rome.   92 **Umbrian**: The Umbrians lived east of the Etruscans.   93 **Gaul**: Cisalpine Gaul bordered the lands of the Etruscans on the north and east.   102 **Horatius**: Horatius is reputed to have been a member of the Lucretian family, one of the three patrician tribes of ancient Rome. The other patrician tribes were the Ramnian and the Titian. In the second stanza following, Spurius Lartius and Herminius are represented as belonging respectively to these two latter families.   114 **strait**: narrow.   142 **Tuscan**: Etruscan.   157 **three chiefs**: The three champions who are described in the next stanza, as well as the three mentioned in the third stanza following, are fictitious. The various places which they are depicted as representing lay within the territories of the Etruscan confederation.   198 **hinds**: peasants.   209 **Astur**: The character of Astur was invented by Macaulay. Luna was a seaport at the east end of the Gulf of Genoa.   221 **she-wolf's litter**: according to tradition, Romulus and Remus, the founders of

kome, were nursed by a she-wolf.   245 **Mount Alvernus**: a
mountain in the Apennines, near the source of the Tiber.   249
augurs: priests believed to have the power of foretelling the future.
257 **Lucumo**: Etruscan chieftain.   292 **Sextus**: the eldest son of
Tarquin, whose evil conduct had been responsible to a considerable
degree for the banishment of the Tarquins from the City.   340
the broad flood: The Tiber at this point is about a hundred yards
wide, and ordinarily is eight or ten feet deep.   349 **Palatinus**:
one of the seven hills of Rome, on which, in early times, were the
homes of most of the patricians.   375 **armour**: Armour of this
period was made of leather or woven fabric.   403 **corn-land**:
public land which ordinarily was rented by the state to private
persons.   411 **Comitium**: an open space in Rome, used for public assembly. It adjoined the Forum and later was incorporated in
it.   414 **halting**: limping. Horatius had been wounded in the
thigh by Astur.   422 **Volscian**: The Volscians were an important
tribe who lived south of the Romans. In early days the two
races were constantly at war.   423 **Juno**: in Roman mythology,
the wife of Jupiter and the goddess of women and of marriage.
433 **Algidus**: a wooded mountain about fifteen miles east of Rome.

THE ICE FLOES

194   Written in 1920. The disaster related in this poem actually
happened to the sealer, *The Greenland*, in the North Atlantic off the
coast of southern Labrador in the spring of 1893. The poet, who
was living in St. John's, Newfoundland, at the time, witnessed the
return of the ship with her flag flying at half-mast, and, with a
group of other boys, stood in the crowded street listening to the
tolling of the church bells during the funeral service.   1 **foretop**:
a partly enclosed look-out platform high on the foremast.   1
barrel: a partly enclosed look-out platform high on the mainmast.
3 **master-watch**: principal look-out man, stationed aloft at the
point of best vision.   7 **slob**: soft ice.   7 **growler**: hard ice.
8 **patch**: large area of ice.   10 **"white harps"**: baby seals,
especially prized for their glossy white pelts. After the seals are
about ten days old, the pelts begin to turn brown, thus becoming less
valuable.   25 **"bobbing-holes"**: air holes, always left open by
the parent seals.   41 **watches**: divisions of the crew.   42
carouse: gay excitement.   46 **caribou**: a kind of reindeer.   48
bill: hooked point.   56 **watch's flag**: flag to indicate the muster-
ing-point of a particular group of seal hunters.   57 **begrimed**:
soiled.   57 **reek**: offensive odour.   62 **pans**: expanses of flat
ice.   64 **donkey-winch**: small portable auxiliary steam engine
used for hoisting.   68 **"sculped"**: skinned.   78 **pan**: pile of

sealskins left temporarily on the ice.   92 **sirene**: siren, whistle.
94 **slipping**: hurriedly releasing.   146 **to lower the price of
bread**: to provide food. For a successful season's sealing, a member
of a ship's crew would be paid about three hundred dollars.

THE CROW AND THE NIGHTHAWK

199   Written in 1943.   3 **bedded down**: laid out.   8 **distillery**: building where whiskey is made.   10 **stance**: the position
taken by the golfer as he prepares to hit the ball.   10 **follow-
through**: the completion of his swing by the golfer after hitting the
ball.   16 **fairway**: mown part of the golf course.   24 **hook**:
a stroke in which the ball curves to the left of the intended line of
flight.   24 **slice**: a stroke in which the ball curves to the right
of the intended line of flight.   25 **rough**: any portion of the golf
course which is not mown.   26 **cheeky**: impudent.   26 **guff**:
banter.   41 **yeggs**: robbers.   49 **zoom**: swoop suddenly and
rapidly upward after flying horizontally at a low level.   78 **fag**:
cigarette.   110 **bivouackers**: persons spending the night in the
out-of-doors.   117 **fuse**: cord which is lighted to explode the
firecracker.   123 **ceiling**: greatest height at which an aircraft
can maintain horizontal flight.   143 **blitz**: sudden overwhelming
attack.

THE BROTHERS

204   7 **pit-props**: wooden timbers supporting or reinforcing the
roof of a mine.   75 **damp**: carbon monoxide gas. It is also
known as after-damp.   103 **hunkers**: haunches.   120 **daft**:
crazy.   122 **cage**: lift, elevator.   124 **pithead**: mine entrance.
143 **he'd slipped**: An ancient superstition is that a mishap of any
kind happening to a miner on his way to work is an omen of mis-
fortune that day.   145 **whippet**: a small, swift breed of dog,
trained for racing.   153 **placed the field**: assigned the players to
their positions.   155 **up to form**: in condition to play well.
177 **within his oxter**: under his arm.   179 **fall**: tackle.

THE MOUNTAIN WHIPPOORWILL

210   The incident related in this modern ballad is represented as
taking place in the State of Georgia, which is located on the Atlantic
seaboard of the United States between South Carolina and Florida.
Whippoorwill: a shy night bird of the eastern United States and
Canada, known for its plaintive and persistent call.   **Hill-Billy**:
the name applied, often slightingly, to a backwoods mountain

255

dweller of the south-eastern United States.   2 **slewin'**: sighing.
This is a local term peculiar to the natives of this particular region,
as are many of the other expressions in the poem.   7 **raised a
pet**: complained.   10 **cockleburs**: The cocklebur is a coarse weed
with purple bur-like flower heads.   12 **mountain-laurel**: an ever-
green shrub with glossy leaves and pink or white flowers.   14
a-skitin': darting.   17 **"Kingdom Come"**: from the chorus of an
American folk song.   18 **a-chunkin'**: croaking.   20 **Essex
County**: a fictitious place.   22 **smarty**: clever and confident.
26 **King-pin**: champion.   27 **wall-eye**: eye showing an unusual
amount of white because of being crossed.   30 **bug**: bulge, open
wide.   40 **dead**: lost, gone.   46 **possum**: opossum.   49
"Turkey in the Straw": a popular American folk song.   56 **ruck**:
undistinguished crowd.   56 **bobtailed**: ordinary.   58 **lost
their bicker**: failed. A bicker is a contest.   80 **fazed**: embarrassed,
worried.   83 **big white beard**: clouds or possibly snow.   94
Skunk-cabbage: a broad-leafed weed, known for its objection-
able odour.   94 **bee-gum stump**: stump which is the home of a
hive of wild bees.   105 **Sashay**: a common step in square dancing.
It consists of a peculiar sliding movement forward, in which one
foot is advanced, followed closely by the other.   106 **Flapjacks**:
pancakes.   109 **Fire on the mountains . . .** : This expression and
those occurring in the next six lines are snatches from Southern folk
songs and spirituals.   110 **a-bilin'**: boiling.   121 **mountain-
shoat**: wild pig.   136 **bossed**: mastered.

IF

215 Written in 1910. It is believed that this poem was addressed
to the poet's only son, John, who was thirteen years old at the time.
He was killed in action in France, in September, 1915.   18 **turn**:
throw, cast.   18 **pitch-and-toss**: game of chance in which coins
are pitched at a mark.

LONDON UNDER BOMBARDMENT

216   This poem was published in the London *Daily Telegraph*
in March, 1941. In World War II, between September, 1940, and
May, 1941, the German air force made an all-out effort to cripple
London. In that period, its bomber squadrons, frequently numbering
several hundred planes in a single night, dropped 28,000 tons of
bombs on the city, causing 21,000 civilian casualties and destroying
or damaging beyond repair several thousand buildings. When the
bombing lessened in the late spring of 1941, the city had not been
destroyed and the spirit of its people had not been broken.   8

Piccadilly: Piccadilly Circus, a famous circle in the heart of London, from which radiate a number of the principal streets of the city. 9 **Regent Street and Kingsway**: historic streets in central London.

VESTIGIA

217 Carman wrote this poem in the summer of 1919 following a long walk through the woods and hills of the Catskill Mountains in New York State. Vestigia are visible traces or signs. Here the poet uses the word with the added meaning of "revelations". 23 **making . . . be**: revealing. 24 **kindling ecstasy**: ardent joy.

THIS WAS MY BROTHER

218 Written in 1942. This poem was composed by the poetess in memory of her brother, Lieutenant-Colonel Howard McTavish of the Royal Canadian Engineers, who died in action at Dieppe, August 12, 1942. 2 **Dieppe**: a French seaport on the English Channel between Le Havre and Calais, where, during World War II, a combined British and Canadian raid on German-occupied France was repulsed with unusually heavy casualties. 18 **breach**: gap.

CARGOES

219 Written in 1912. 1 **Quinquereme**: an ancient galley rowed by five banks of oars. 1 **of**: i.e., built in. 1 **Nineveh**: the capital of ancient Assyria, in the Near East. It was one of the great shipping and ship-building centres of early times. 1 **Ophir**: In Old Testament times, Ophir was a country with which the Hebrews traded. Its location is uncertain, but it is usually identified with the south-eastern coast of Arabia. In ancient days a canal connected the Red Sea and the lower Nile. 2 **Palestine**: the Holy Land, at the eastern end of the Mediterranean. 6 **the Isthmus**: Panama, in Spanish America. 10 **cinnamon**: a variety of garnet. 10 **moidores**: The moidore is a Portuguese gold coin. 11 **coaster**: ship used in coastal trade. Such a ship frequently is called a tramp steamer. 12 **Butting**: pushing stubbornly. 12 **Channel**: English Channel. 13 **Tyne**: Newcastle, on the Tyne River in north-eastern England. It is the loading-point of great quantities of manufactured products. 14 **road-rails**: railroad-rails. 14 **pig-lead**: lead in rough bars.

MACAVITY: THE MYSTERY CAT

220 3 **Scotland Yard**: now New Scotland Yard, the head-quarters of the London Metropolitan Police force; hence, the force

itself, especially the detective department.   3 **Flying Squad**: a specially trained body of police, responsible for reaching the scene of a crime in the least possible time.   7 **levitation**: the illusion of raising heavy objects, such as the human body, in the air without means of support.   11 **ginger**: light reddish-yellow.   19 **by-street**: little-frequented street.   24 **Peke**: Pekinese, a kind of small Chinese dog with long silky hair.

THE OLD MILL

223   Written in 1928. The inspiration for this poem came to the poet while he was sitting on a terrace, overlooking the ruined walls of the Old Mill, which stand on the west bank of the Humber River about a mile and a half from the river mouth. The Humber flows into Lake Ontario in the western part of Metropolitan Toronto. The mill was built in the 1830's and did a thriving business until the 1850's, when as a result of declining trade it was closed down and abandoned.   **once-proud walls**: The walls were constructed of broad, flat stones taken from the river. They were admired greatly for their massiveness and height.   7 **wine**: fill.   11 **Words**: See Matthew, Chapter IV, verse 4.   13 **wheels**: circular flat stones, revolved by means of water power and used for grinding the grain.   14 **grist**: ground grain.   19 **amber**: golden grain.

NIGHT-DRIVING

224   2 **crane**: stretch.   4 **pitfalls**: sources of danger.

THE FRUIT-RANCHER

225   The fruit ranch is represented as being in a small valley in south-eastern British Columbia.   15 **Kootenai**: a tributary of the Columbia River.   15 **snakes**: winds, twists.

THE PALATINE

226   The Palatine was one of the seven hills of ancient Rome. The palaces of the Caesars were located on this hill.   5 **Caesar**: the title conferred on the Roman emperors, 27 B.C.-476 A.D. Rome was sacked by the Vandals in 455 A.D. and the last of the emperors deposed not long afterwards.   29 **Gaul**: a Roman province which in ancient times included France and northern Italy.   30 **Dacian**: The Roman province of Dacia lay north of the lower Danube.   37 **Shere-end Hill**: a height of land in Kent, near the mouth of the Thames River.

NOTATION ON IMMORTALITY

227   5 **"Perish as a beast"**: See Psalm XLIX, verse 20.   7
"Without are dogs": See Revelation, Chapter XXII, verse 15. Among
the Jews the dog was despised, being declared unclean by their law.

VITAI LAMPADA

228   The title, taken from early Latin, means "the torch of life".
The poet was thinking of the Grecian torch race—much like the
modern relay race—in which each contestant carried a lighted
torch, which, as he finished his leg of the course, he handed on to
the next runner in the relay.   1 **Close**: school playground. An
uneven playing-field, causing the ball to bounce irregularly when
bowled to the batter.   3 **a bumping pitch**: an irregularly bouncing
ball.   3 **a blinding light**: the glare of the sinking sun.   5 **a
ribboned coat**: given to the members of a winning team, just as
lettered sweaters frequently are in Canada and the United States.
11 **Gatling**: a kind of early machine gun.   18 **the School**:
The poet was thinking of his own school, Clifton, most of whose
graduating year usually passed directly into military schools.

INDEX BY AUTHORS

INDEX BY AUTHORS

263

265

ACKNOWLEDGMENTS

ACKNOWLEDGMENTS

For permission to use copyrighted material grateful acknowledgment is made to the following authors and publishers:

Appleton-Century-Crofts, Inc., for "Night-Driving" by A. E. M., from Gordon and King: *Verse of Our Day*.

Mrs. George Bambridge, for "If" by Rudyard Kipling, from *Rewards and Fairies*.

Basil Blackwell & Mott, Ltd., for "Wander-Thirst" by Gerald Gould.

William Blackwood & Sons, Ltd., and Alfred Noyes, for "The Highwayman", "The Admiral's Ghost" and "*Kilmeny*", from *The Collected Poems of Alfred Noyes*.

Arthur S. Bourinot, for "Johnny Appleseed" from *This Green Earth*, and "Paul Bunyan".

Chatto & Windus, Ltd., for "Lone Dog" by Irene Rutherford McLeod, from *Songs to Save a Soul*.

Clarke, Irwin & Company Limited, for "The Trapper and the Bears" by Watson Kirkconnell, from *The Flying Bull and Other Tales*.

Coward-McCann, Inc., for "Daniel Webster's Horses" by Elizabeth Coatsworth, from *Compass Rose*. Copyright 1929 by Coward-McCann, Inc.

J. M. Dent & Sons (Canada) Ltd., for "The Donkey" by G. K. Chesterton, from *The Wild Knight and Other Poems*.

Faber & Faber, Ltd., and Walter de la Mare, for "Sam's Three Wishes", and "Old Susan".

Faber & Faber, Ltd., and T. S. Eliot, for "Macavity: the Mystery Cat" from *Old Possum's Book of Practical Cats*.

Gene Fowler, for "The *Jervis Bay* Goes Down".

W. W. Gibson, for "The Brothers", "Flannan Isle" and "The Lighthouse", from *Collected Poems, 1905-1925*.

272

The Ryerson Press, for "The Little Boats of Britain" by Sara Carsley, from *The Artisan*; for "The Fruit-Rancher" from *I Sing of Life*, by Lloyd Roberts; for "The *Laughing Sally*" from *Selected Poems of Sir Charles G. D. Roberts*; for "The Forsaken" and "On the Way to the Mission" from *Selected Poems of Duncan Campbell Scott*; and for "The Cremation of Sam McGee" and "The Shooting of Dan McGrew" from *The Complete Poems of Robert W. Service*.

Robert J. C. Stead, for "The Squad of One".

Nancy Byrd Turner, for "Lincoln", from *Child Life Magazine*; and for "Notation on Immortality", from *The Atlantic Monthly*.

St. Martin's Classsics

BAROMETER RISING. By HUGH MACLENNAN
A distinguished Canadian novel skilfully edited with notes, character studies, and study questions. Suitable for Senior High School grades.

THE BLACK ARROW. By ROBERT LOUIS STEVENSON
Edited with Introduction and Notes and Questions by EMSLEY L. YEO, M.A. Illustrated by H. M. BROCK.

A BOOK OF GOOD STORIES
Edited with Introduction and Notes by G. FRED McNALLY, M.A.

THE CALL OF THE WILD. By JACK LONDON
With an Introduction, Notes and Bibliography by DORA WHITEFIELD.

CAPTAINS COURAGEOUS. By RUDYARD KIPLING

FLIGHT INTO DANGER and Other Plays. In preparation
Edited with Introduction and Notes by HERMAN VOADEN.
A well-balanced anthology of four modern full-length plays from Canada, the United States and England.

THE GOLDEN DOG. By WILLIAM KIRBY
Shortened, with Introduction and Glossary by E. C. WOODLEY, M.A.

THE GREAT ADVENTURER. By PEGGY ALBION-MEEK
A fresh and lively narrative of the Trojan War, combining the *Iliad* and the *Odyssey*. Introduction, notes, questions by W. J. ELLISON, Weston Collegiate and Vocational School.

HEROIC TALES IN VERSE
Edited with Introduction and Notes by E. J. PRATT, M.A., Ph.D. A collection of long narrative poems for use in Secondary Schools.

INVITATION TO DRAMA
Selected and edited by ANDREW A. ORR. A collection of one-act plays for Secondary Schools.

INVITATION TO POETRY. By J. L. GILL and L. H. NEWELL
This anthology is in a new attractive format. It contains many new poems as well as old favourites. The selections are both light and serious and offer a balanced representation of Canadian, American and English verse. The book is in two parallel parts for use in consecutive years. With detailed, accurate notes.

IVANHOE. By SIR WALTER SCOTT
Edited and abridged by FANNY JOHNSON. Illustrated.

THE JUNGLE BOOK. By RUDYARD KIPLING
Illustrated by J. LOCKWOOD KIPLING and W. H. DRAKE.

KIM. By RUDYARD KIPLING
Illustrated by J. LOCKWOOD KIPLING. School edition with
copyrighted glossary available only in Canada. Mimeo-
graphed notes by LINTON D. READ, Belleville Collegiate and
Vocational School, available on request.

LOST HORIZON. By JAMES HILTON
Notes "About the Author".

MARIA CHAPDELAINE. By LOUIS HÉMON
Translated and with an Introduction by W. H. BLAKE.
Foreword by HUGH EAYRS.

MASTER SKYLARK. By JOHN BENNETT
With an Introduction, Notes and Questions by H. W.
CHRYSLER, Head of the Department of English, Oakwood
Collegiate Institute, Toronto. Illustrated.

NEIGHBOURS UNKNOWN. By CHARLES G. D. ROBERTS
With an Introduction by J. M. GRAY. Illustrated by
PAUL BRANSON.

NEW HARVESTING. Edited by ETHEL HUME BENNETT
A collection of contemporary Canadian poetry.

THE OPEN ROAD—Essays, Stories and Travel Tales. By
R. L. HALE
A Prose Anthology for Grade XI students including
selections by Stephen Leacock, W. W. Jacobs, O. Henry,
Sir Winston Churchill and others. With notes and
questions.

THE PEARL. By JOHN STEINBECK
A powerful story of a Mexican family and of the pearl that
completely changes their lives. With notes, questions by
R. L. HALE and P. A. DE SOUZA of Peterborough Collegiate
Institute.

A PEDLAR'S PACK—Narrative Poetry
Selected and Edited by ADRIAN MACDONALD, M.A.

POEMS OF YESTERDAY AND TO-DAY
Ninety-four selections from the works of sixty-six poets,
including Browning. Tennyson, Burns, Noyes, Colum,
Kipling, Newbolt, Masefield, de la Mare, Bridges, Drink-
water, Christina Rossetti, Charles G. D. Roberts and
Carman.

PROSE OF OUR DAY—Revised Edition. Edited by J. M
GRAY, F. A. UPJOHN and J. J. KNIGHTS
A carefully balanced selection containing forty-five
examples of modern prose of all types. Twenty-three
of the items are by British authors, twelve by American
and ten by Canadian.

THE RED BADGE OF COURAGE. By STEPHEN CRANE
This classic portrayal of the psychology of a man on a
battlefield, during the American Civil War, will appeal
to senior students in Grades XI-XII, through its vividly
described episodes in which action and human emotions
play a large and effective part. With Notes and Questions
by B. C. DILTZ of the Ontario College of Education.

SELECTED STORIES FROM CANADIAN PROSE
Prose selections from the works of Judge Haliburton,
Pauline Johnson, Agnes Laut, Duncan Campbell Scott,
Gilbert Parker, Charles G. D. Roberts, Louis Hémon,
L. M. Montgomery, Mazo de la Roche and others.

SILAS MARNER. By GEORGE ELIOT
Edited with Introduction and Notes by G. FRED MC-
NALLY, M.A. Illustrated.

A TALE OF TWO CITIES. By CHARLES DICKENS
With an Introduction by G. K. CHESTERTON and Notes
and Questions by GUY BOAS. Illustrated.

TEN SELECTED POEMS. By E. J. PRATT
Contains three long narratives, including most of *Brébeuf
and his Brethren*, and seven other popular choices, edited
with notes by the author.

TREASURE ISLAND. By ROBERT LOUIS STEVENSON
With an Introduction and Notes. Illustrated by H. M.
Brock.

TWENTY-ONE MODERN ESSAYS
Edited with Introduction and Notes by J. F. MACDONALD,
M.A. Modern essays, English, American and Canadian,
specially selected for the middle and upper grades of
Secondary Schools.

TWO SOLITUDES. By HUGH MACLENNAN
Suitably abridged for Secondary School use. With Notes
and Questions by DR. CLAUDE T. BISSELL.

THE VICAR OF WAKEFIELD. By OLIVER GOLDSMITH
With an Introduction and Notes by J. F. MACDONALD,
M.A. Illustrated by HUGH THOMSON.